Puzzling Picture

Match the jigsaw pieces to where they belong to complete the picture of Moana, Pua and Heihei on the beach.

a

b

c

d

Mermaid Differences

Which image of Ariel, Flounder and Sebastian is different?

a

b

c

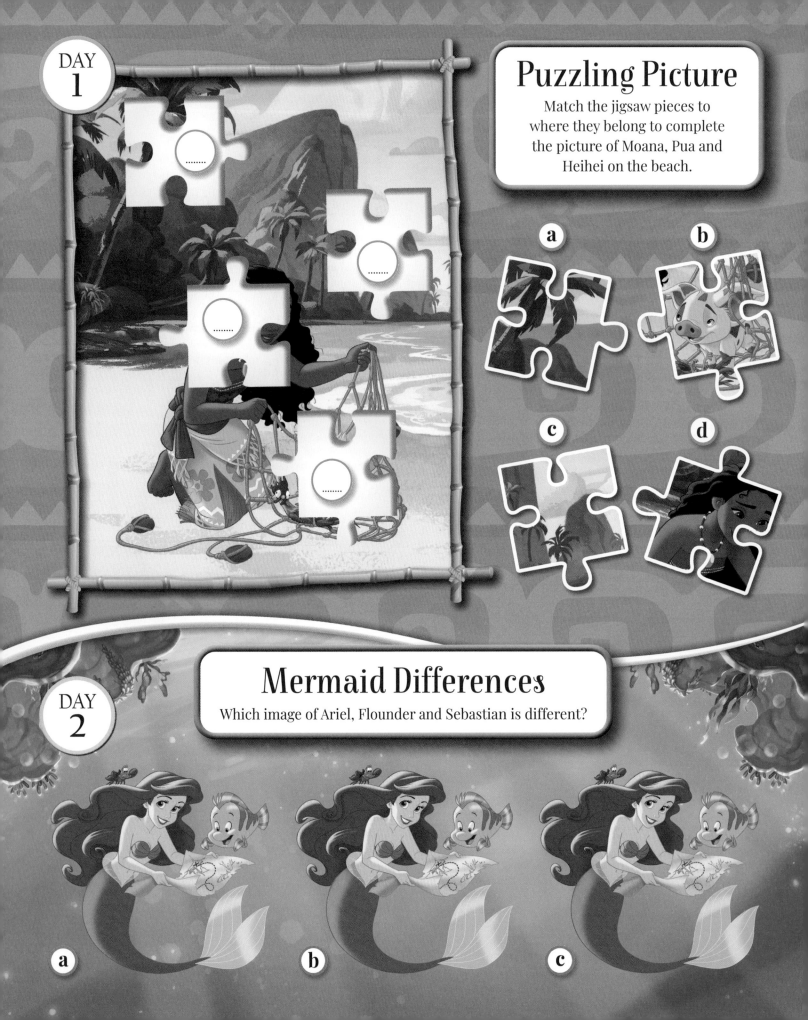

DAY 3

Dress Dot-to-Dot

Connect the dots to complete Tiana's beautiful dress!

DAY 4

Mouse Maze

Following the sequence, guide Gus and Jaq through the button maze to reach Cinderella.

Sequence

START

FINISH

Merida Mix-up

DAY 5

Help Merida to sort out her arrows by counting
how many of each colour arrow there are below.

Servant Shadows

DAY 6

Can you match the Enchanted Servants
to their correct shadows?

ⓐ ⓑ ⓒ ⓓ

① ② ③ ④

Pretty Patterns

Aurora is taking a stroll in the woods. Look closely and see if you can help her to complete these sequences.

1

2

3

4

a b c d

Hero Sketch

Using the image on the left as a guide, draw a picture of Mulan!

START

Which Lamp?

Discover which lamp Jasmine needs to summon the Genie by following the clues below.

Clues

1. Move left two spaces
2. Move up two spaces
3. Move right two spaces
4. Move up two spaces
5. Move left three spaces
6. Move down three spaces
7. Move left one space

Snow Scramble

Help Snow White unscramble the letters to discover the names of the Seven Dwarfs!

yopde

ezenys

odc

hblusaf

mrugpy

ahpyp

pslyee

Perfect Palette

Which paint palette matches the bigger palette exactly?

b

d

a

c

e

Pocahontas Picture

Use your best crayons to decorate this
scene of Pocahontas and Meeko!

a
b
c
d
e

Cinderella Close-ups

Look at the close-ups and see if you can match them to where they belong in the image of Cinderella and her dog, Bruno.

....
....
....
....
....

Spot the Difference

There are eight differences between these two images of Mulan. Can you spot them all?

DAY 15

START

FINISH

Te Fiti Track

Find a path through the maze to restore the heart of Te Fiti. Make sure you go over every stone once!

DAY 16

Sea Sudoku

Help Ariel to complete this sudoku puzzle! There can only be one of each character in every row and column.

a

b

c

Beautiful Butterflies

Pocahontas is a friend to nature! How many pink and purple butterflies can you count in this woodland scene?

Purple Butterflies

○ ....

Pink Butterflies

○ ....

Friend Finder

Look at the close-ups to the left and find where Cinderella's animal friends are in the scene.

1 ....
2 ....
3 ....
4 ....
5 ....

Tiana Changes

One of these images of Tiana is slightly different to the others. Look closely and see if you can spot which one!

a **b** **c**

Noughts and Crosses

Playing with a friend, choose who will be noughts and who will be crosses. Then, take turns filling in empty spaces in the grid. The winner is the first player to fill three spaces in a row horizontally, vertically or diagonally.

Trouble Trail

Merida needs to find her little brothers before they cause trouble! Help her by matching the pieces at the bottom of the page to where they belong in the trail. Be careful, one doesn't belong!

DAY 21

START

FINISH

1 ....
2 ....
3 ....
4 ....
5 ....

a b c d e f

Princess Picture

Add some colour to this picture of Jasmine reading her favourite book.

DAY 22

DAY 23

a

b

c

d

The Real Belle

Follow the clues below to discover which image is really Belle.

Clues

1. The real Belle is not reading a book with a purple cover

2. The real Belle has a blue bow in her hair

3. The real Belle is not wearing grey shoes

Take Note!

Follow the green lines to discover which musical notes Rapunzel needs to write a new song. Draw the notes in the spaces below.

START

FINISH

DAY 24

DAY 25

Fan Finder

There's one fan that only appears once in the jumble below. Can you find it?

DAY 26

Princess Puzzle

Complete this puzzle by working out which squares should contain bluebirds, and which are empty! The numbers in the circles tell you how many bluebirds there should be in each row and column. Snow White has started the puzzle for you! Hint: start with row 'o' and add the Xs!

Jigsaw Jumble

Pocahontas is spending time with her animal friends, Meeko and Flit. Match the jigsaw pieces to the spaces to complete the scene.

a

b

d

c

Treasure Tracker

DAY 28

Ariel loves to collect treasures from the human world. How many of each item can you find in her grotto?

a

b

c

d

e

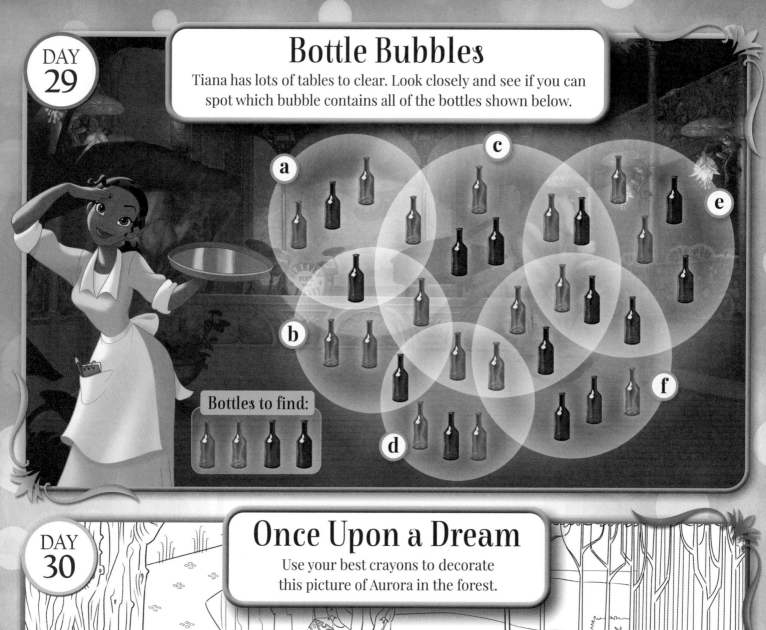

Bottle Bubbles

DAY 29

Tiana has lots of tables to clear. Look closely and see if you can spot which bubble contains all of the bottles shown below.

a b c d e f

Bottles to find:

Once Upon a Dream

DAY 30

Use your best crayons to decorate this picture of Aurora in the forest.

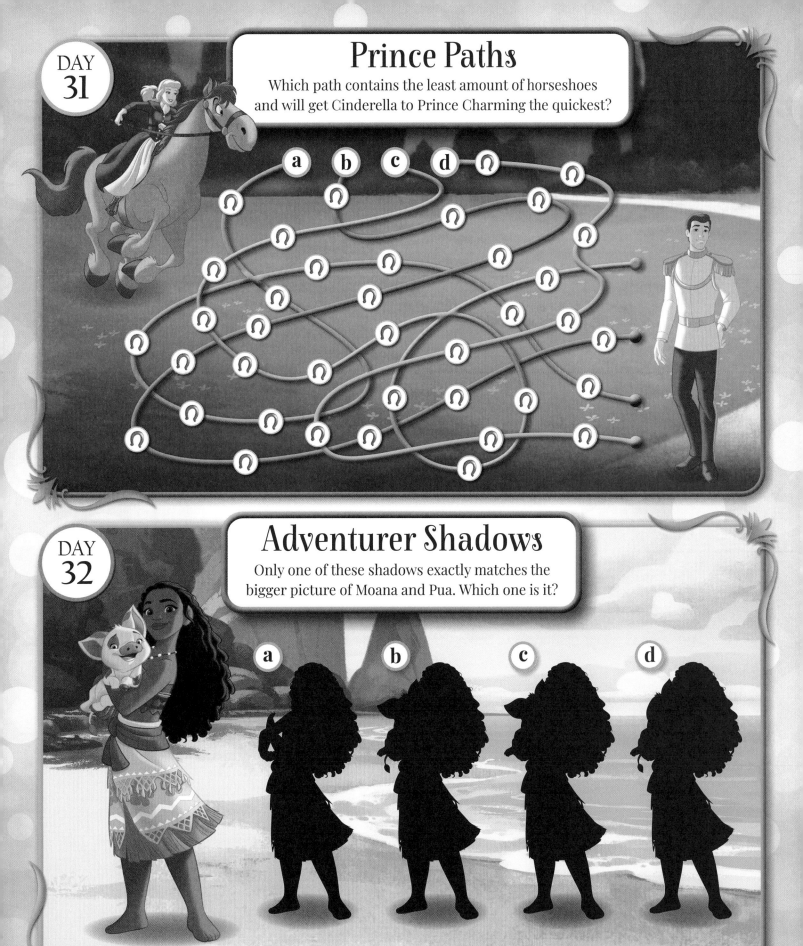

Prince Paths

DAY 31

Which path contains the least amount of horseshoes and will get Cinderella to Prince Charming the quickest?

a   b   c   d

Adventurer Shadows

DAY 32

Only one of these shadows exactly matches the bigger picture of Moana and Pua. Which one is it?

a   b   c   d

a   b   c

A Small Change

Can you spot which image of Merida is slightly different to the others?

Castle Close-ups

Belle is reading to the Enchanted Servants of the castle. Which of the close-ups below does not belong in the picture?

a   b   c

d   e

Sequence Search

Can you spot all the sequences in the puzzle? Jasmine has done the first one for you.

Example:

b

a

c

d

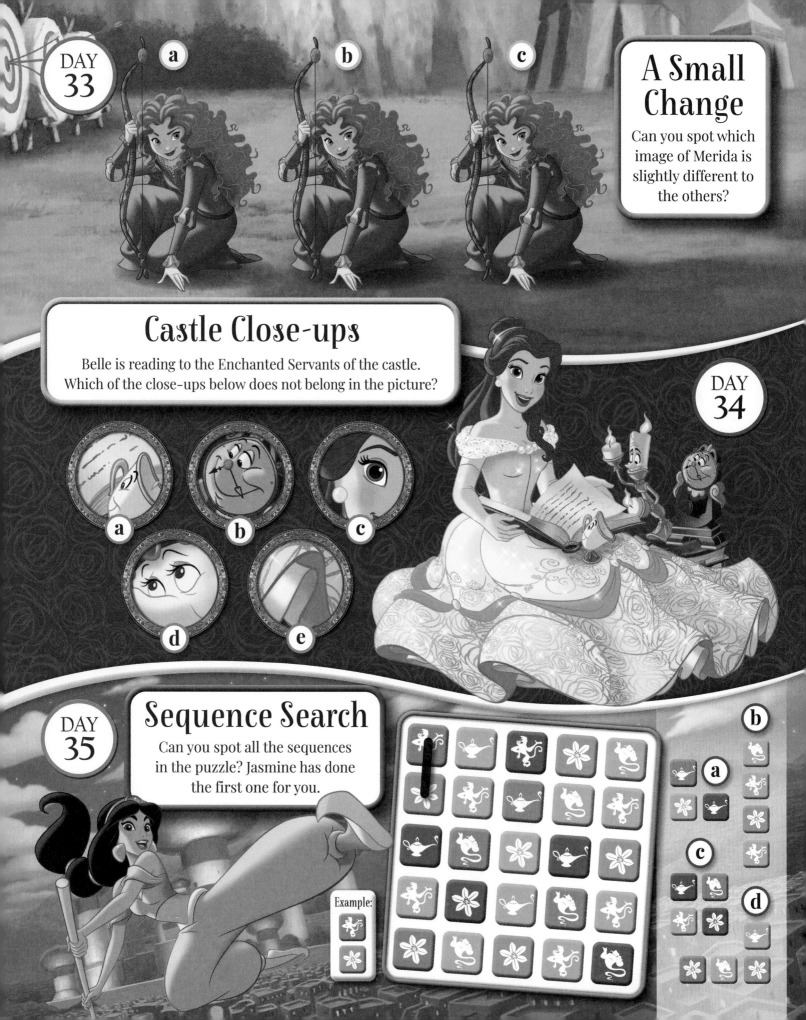

Domino Dash

Complete Rapunzel's path of dominoes by working out where the pieces at the bottom of the page belong.

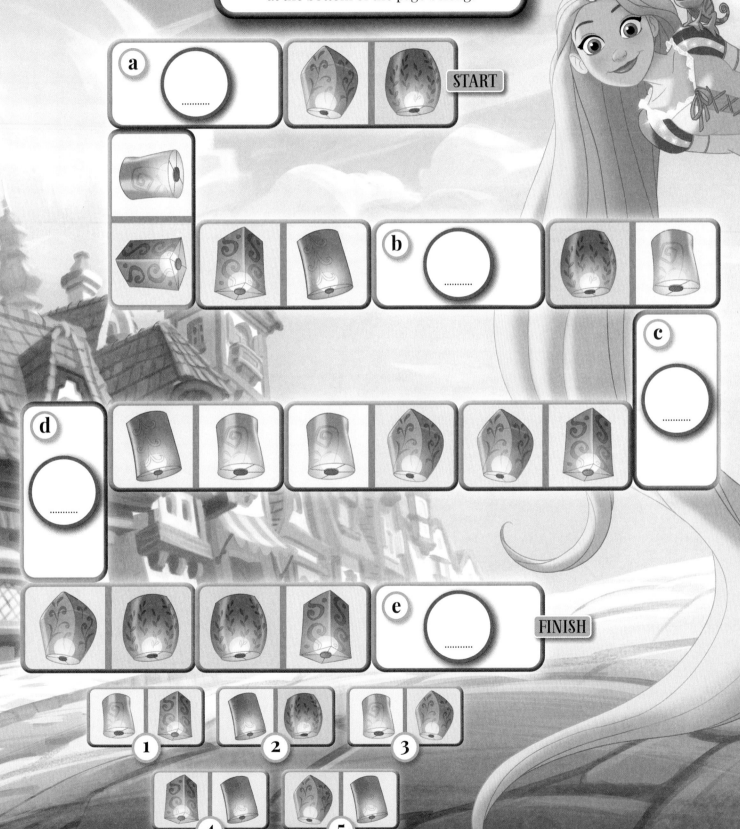

DAY
37

Dinner Time!

It's dinner time in the Dwarfs' cottage.
Follow the line mazes to discover which
bowl belongs to which Dwarf.

a b c

1 2 3

DAY
38

Picture Jumble

This magical picture of the Fairy
Godmother transforming Cinderella's
dress is all jumbled up! Labelling the pieces
from 1 to 5, can you put it back in order?

a b c d e

Dot-to-Dot Fun
Connect the dots to complete this wonderful picture of Pocahontas!

Which Bone?

Only one of these sums is correct. Circle the right answer to discover which is Little Brother's bone!

a) 5 x 10 =   45

b) 9 x 4 =   37

c) 4 x 11 =   44

d) 6 x 7 =   41

DAY
41

Colour by Numbers

Using your crayons and the colour key on the right,
decorate this picture of Ariel and Flounder.

1
2
3
4
5
6

DAY
42

Silhouette Sorter

Help Aurora to sort out these silhouettes by
drawing lines between the ones that match!

Father Finds

DAY 43

Chief Tui is looking for Moana! Guide him through the maze to find his daughter.

START

FINISH

Carpet Copy

DAY 44

Which Magic Carpet matches the bigger image exactly?

a

b

c

d

Bingo with Belle

Help Belle to find which of the smaller bingo cards exactly matches the bigger one!

Chameleon Counter

How many of each pose of Pascal can you count in the jumble?

Scotland Scene

Merida is brilliant at archery! Use your crayons to colour this scene.

Dwarf Dilemma

Look at the close-ups and see if you can work out which Dwarf they belong to.

a   b   c   d

Number Key

Mermaid Maths

Using the key on the left, can you help Ariel
and Flounder to complete these underwater sums?

1

2

3

4

5

6

+ − = a

....

+ + = b

....

− + = c

....

+ + = d

....

Tic-Tac-Toe

Playing with a friend, decide who will be noughts and
who will be crosses. Take it in turns to fill in an empty space
on the grid. The winner is the first person to fill three
spaces in a row horizontally, vertically or diagonally.

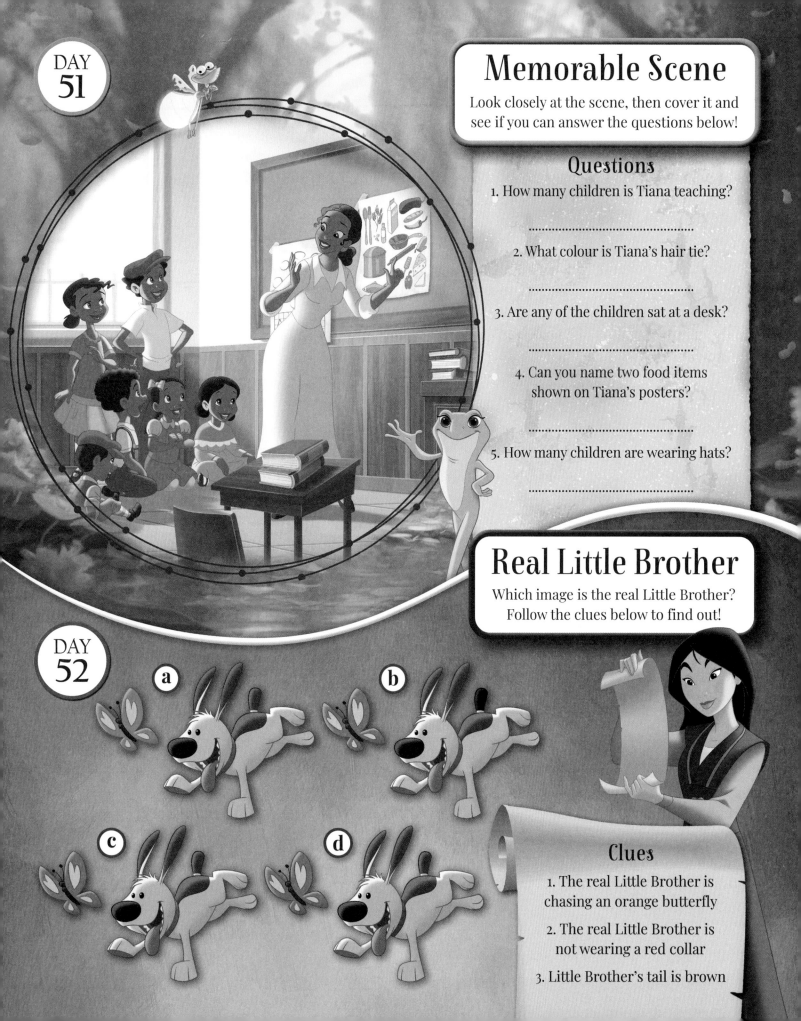

DAY 51

Memorable Scene

Look closely at the scene, then cover it and see if you can answer the questions below!

Questions

1. How many children is Tiana teaching?

....

2. What colour is Tiana's hair tie?

....

3. Are any of the children sat at a desk?

....

4. Can you name two food items shown on Tiana's posters?

....

5. How many children are wearing hats?

....

Real Little Brother

Which image is the real Little Brother? Follow the clues below to find out!

DAY 52

ⓐ   ⓑ

ⓒ   ⓓ

Clues

1. The real Little Brother is chasing an orange butterfly

2. The real Little Brother is not wearing a red collar

3. Little Brother's tail is brown

Spot the Difference

There are eight differences between these images of Cinderella and her mouse friends! Can you spot them all?

Let's Surf

Moana and Pua love surfing through the ocean! Use your best pencils to bring this picture to life.

Marketplace Mayhem

Complete the picture of Jasmine and Aladdin strolling through the marketplace by working out where the jigsaw pieces belong in the scene.

a   b

d

c

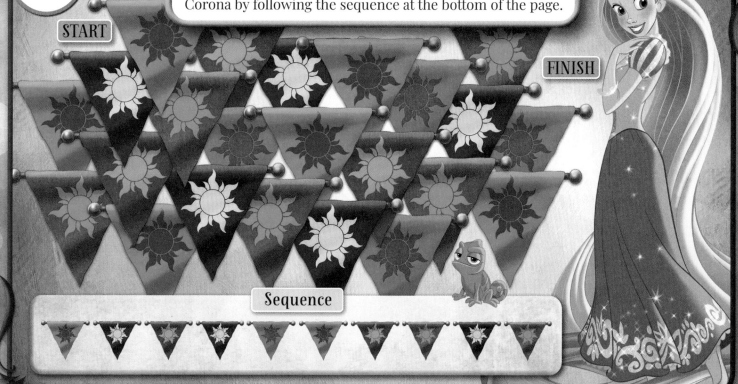

Royal Flag Route

Help Rapunzel to find the correct path through the flags of Corona by following the sequence at the bottom of the page.

START

FINISH

Sequence

Height Help

DAY 57

Help Aurora to put these animals in height order by labelling them from 1 to 6, with 1 being the smallest and 6 being the tallest.

a ...... b ...... c ...... d ...... e ...... f ......

Will o' the Wisp Way

DAY 58

Guide Merida to Elinor Bear, making sure she goes over every will o' the wisp.

START

FINISH

Post Pile

DAY 59

Belle loves writing letters to her friends! How many blue envelopes with purple stamps can you find in the pile of letters waiting to be posted?

Snow White Sequences

Help Snow White to complete these
sequences by filling in all the empty spaces!

1.

2.

3.

4.

5.

6.

a · b · c · d · e · f

Mulan Message

Mulan has received a secret message! Use the code below to help her work out what it says.

a b c d e f g h i j k

l m n o p q r s t

u v w x y z

_ _ _ _   _ _ _ _ _ _   _ _ _ _   _ _ _ _ _ _

Food Favourites

Naveen, Eudora and Charlotte love Tiana's food, but what is their favourite? Find out by following the line mazes!

1

2

3

a

b

c

DAY 63

Ariel Art
Complete this dot-to-dot of Ariel, then colour her in!

Once Upon a Time...
In the space below, write an exciting short story about Pocahontas!

DAY 64

Word Finder

How many times can you find
the word **JASMINE** in the grid below?

J A S M I N E J
E N B E Q W K A
R M O R V P S S
J A S M I N E M
N Y I G E L E I
S A E M D N D N
J A S M I N E E
Q J A S M I N E

Jasmine appears .... times!

Mermaid Match

Only three of these images
of Ariel match exactly. Can you
spot which ones?

a   b   c

d   e   f

Wayfinder Wardrobe

In the space below, draw a brand new outfit for Moana to wear on her next adventure.

Companion Counting

Cinderella loves spending time with her mice friends. How many mice can you count in this scene?

There are

....

mice!

Target Practice

Merida loves practising her archery. Now see if you can hit the target! Close your eyes and using your finger try to hit as close to the bullseye as possible. Have three attempts, making sure to mark where you land as you go!

Shadow of a Hero

Which of these shadows is exactly the same as the bigger picture of Mulan?

a **b** **c** **d**

A Nice Spot of Tea

Colour this scene of Belle with Mrs Potts and Chip!

Bird Trail

Using the key, help Aurora to find her way through the birds!

START

FINISH

↑ → ← ↓

A Work of Art

In the space below, draw a picture of anything you like. Then, colour it in!

Beautiful Birds

Jasmine and Rajah are spending time in the palace gardens. How many birds are around them?

There are .... birds!

DAY 75

START

Tiana Track

Naveen is trying to catch up with Tiana! Guide him through the maze to her, making sure he goes over every bunch of flowers.

FINISH

DAY 76

Baking Differences

Snow White loves baking for the Dwarfs. Can you spot eight differences between these scenes?

Mouse Masterpiece

Using the grid to help you, draw a lovely picture of Cinderella's mouse friend, Jaq!

Pet Poses

How many of each pose of Flit flying through the forest can you count?

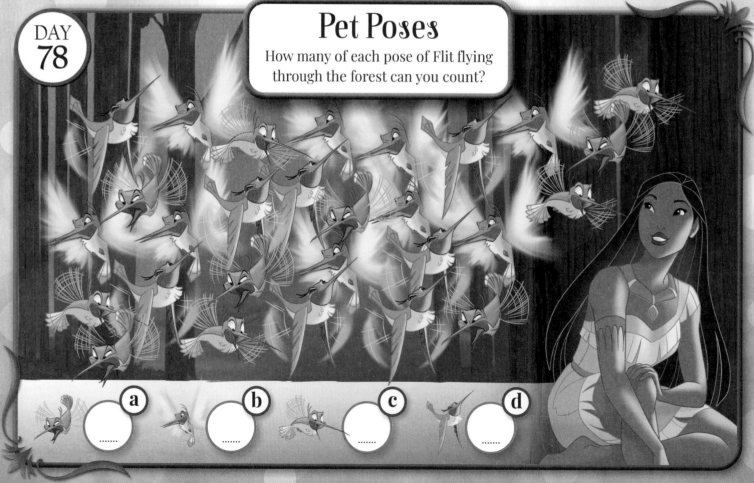

a ....

b ....

c ....

d ....

Ariel's Treasures

Look at the list of items. Can you spot these four things in Princess Ariel's bedroom? Circle each one when you find it!

Things to find

1. Hair comb
2. Purple cushion
3. Umbrella
4. Pair of slippers

Set Sail!

Find a route through the grid from Moana to Maui, making sure to go over every sailboat only once.

START

FINISH

DAY 81

Jigsaw Joy

Place the puzzle pieces in the correct spaces to complete this picture of Aurora and Phillip dancing outside the castle.

a

b

c

Dancing Difference

One of these images of Jasmine dancing is slightly different from the others! Which one is it?

a

b

c

DAY 82

DAY 83

Snow Scene

Dopey is listening to Snow White read his favourite fairy tale. Use your crayons to decorate the picture!

Terrific Tale

Belle loves reading! In the space below, write an exciting
story for her to enjoy. Be as imaginative as you can!

Once upon a time...

_____

_____

_____

_____

_____

_____

_____

_____

_____

_____

_____

The End

All Square

Playing with a friend,
take it in turns to join two dots
with a line. Each new line
must connect with a line that
is already on the board. If you
draw a line that completes a
square, write your initial inside
it. The game continues until
all the squares are completed.
The winner is the person with
the most squares.

Princess Painting

Decorate this scene of Rapunzel
using your best pencils!

DAY 87

Scene It All

Look closely at the scene on the left, then cover it and see if you can answer the questions below!

Questions

1. How many ornaments are there on the fireplace?

....

2. What colour is Merida's coat?

....

3. Is Merida's sword in the room?

....

4. Is the floor made of wood or stone?

....

Perfect Puzzle

Complete Tiana's sudoku puzzle by ensuring there is only one of each icon in every column and row!

DAY 88

Triton Trail

DAY 89

Guide Ariel to her father, King Triton, by finding the path with the most amount of icons.

a

b

c

Mess Mayhem

DAY 90

The Dwarfs are super messy! Help Snow White to pair up their hats by drawing lines between the ones that match.

DAY 91

Pocahontas Path

Meeko is looking for Pocahontas. Follow the sequence below to find the correct path through the grid.

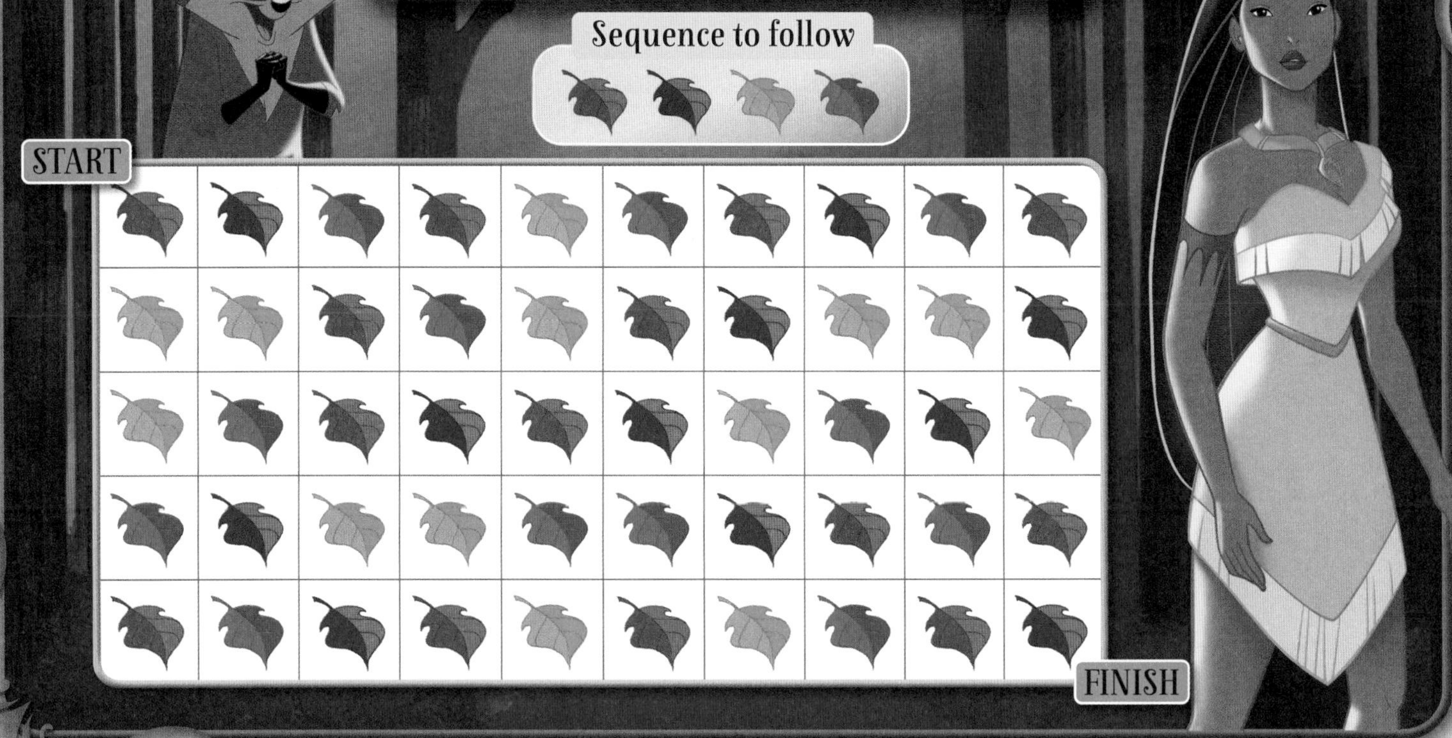
Sequence to follow
START
FINISH

DAY 92

Magic Mirror Match

The Beast gave Belle the Magic Mirror so she could see her father. Which shadow is exactly the same as the bigger image?

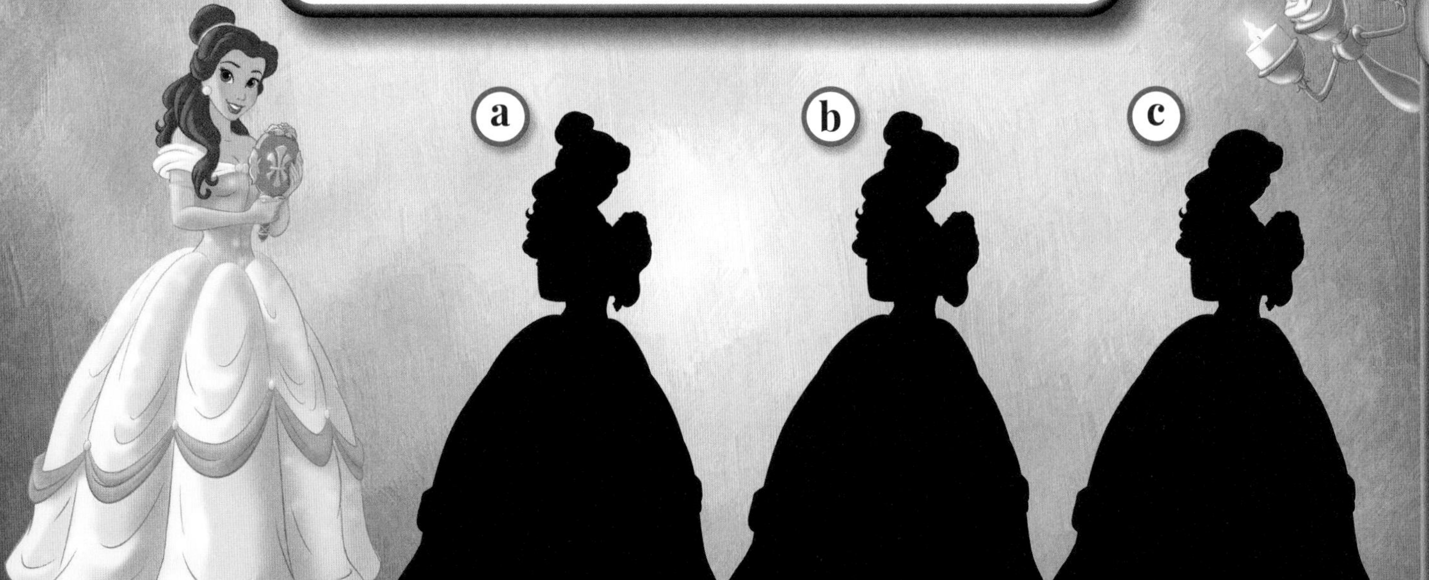
a
b
c

Travel in Style

Cinderella arrived at the Royal Ball in
a beautiful carriage. In the space below,
draw and colour your own carriage.

I am Moana!

Complete this image of Moana and Heihei by working out where each puzzle piece belongs.

DAY 94

a

c

b

Canine Chase

Can you find a route through the maze that will lead Little Brother to Mulan?

DAY 95

START

FINISH

Odd Animal Out

In this scene of Aurora singing for her animal friends, there is one animal that appears once. Which one is it? Circle your answer!

DAY 96

Picture Pieces

Rapunzel is working on a new painting! Put the scene back in the right order by labelling the pieces from 1 to 5.

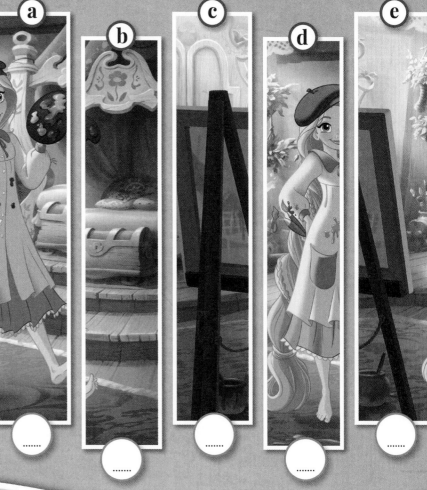

a ....

b ....

c ....

d ....

e ....

Magic Maths

Using the key, can you complete these magical sums?

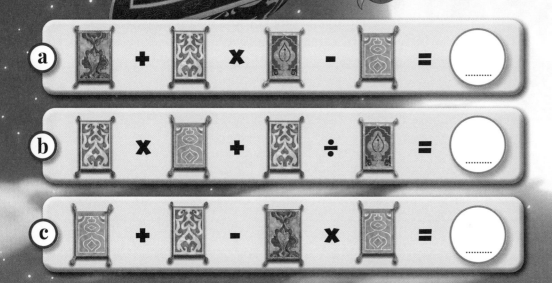

a [ ] + [ ] × [ ] - [ ] = (..........)

b [ ] × [ ] + [ ] ÷ [ ] = (..........)

c [ ] + [ ] - [ ] × [ ] = (..........)

KEY

1   **2**

3   **4**

DAY
99

Exploring Fun

Pocahontas is showing John Smith around her homeland. How many of each object can you count in the jumble?

a ....
b ....
c ....
d ....
e ....

Scottish Secret

DAY
100

Help Merida to work out what the secret message says, using the code to help you!

a b c d e f g h i
j k l m n o p q
r s t u v w x y z

____ ____ ____   ____ ____ ____ ____

____ ____ ____ ____ ____ ____

____ ____ ____ ____ ____ ____ ____   ____ ____ ____

Friendly Firefly

DAY 101

Get creative and draw a wonderful picture of Ray the firefly in the grid on the right.

Wool Way

DAY 102

Follow the key to find the correct way through the maze to help Cinderella finish making her dress!

START→

FINISH

KEY

→ ↓ ← ↑

Diamond Dash

DAY 103

The Dwarfs have finished their day working at the mine! Which path contains the least amount of diamonds and will get them home to Snow White the quickest?

Part of Your World

DAY 104

Use your best crayons to decorate this picture of Ariel on land!

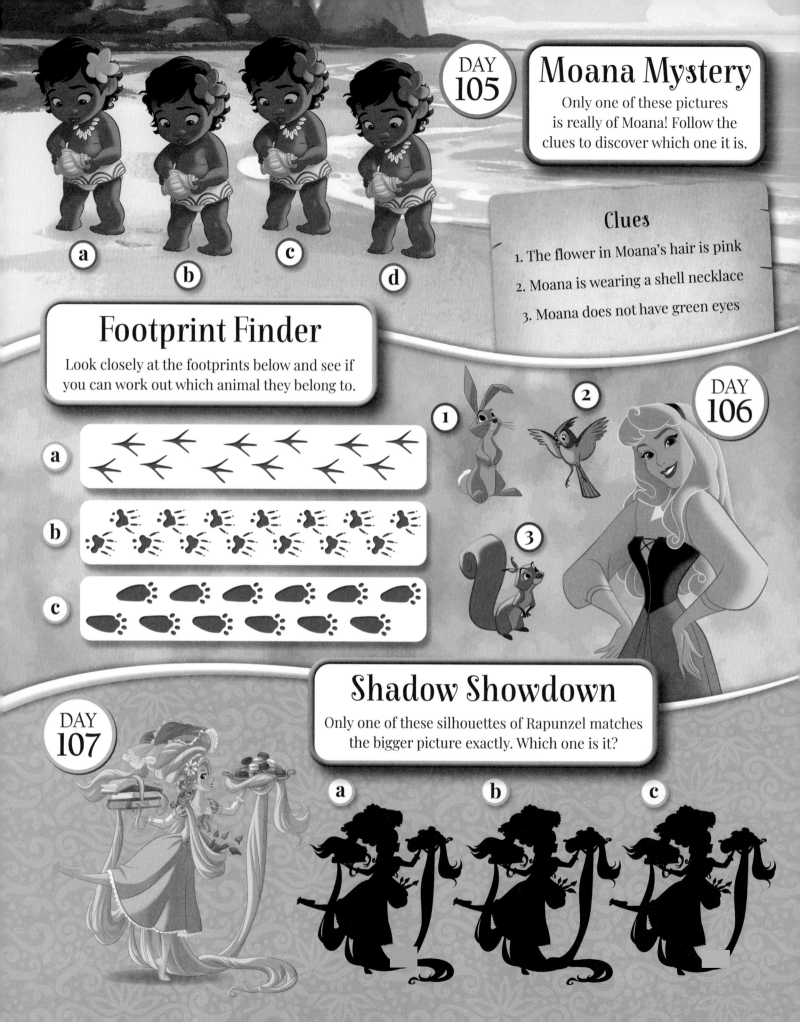

Moana Mystery

Only one of these pictures is really of Moana! Follow the clues to discover which one it is.

a

b

c

d

Clues

1. The flower in Moana's hair is pink

2. Moana is wearing a shell necklace

3. Moana does not have green eyes

Footprint Finder

Look closely at the footprints below and see if you can work out which animal they belong to.

a

b

c

1

2

3

Shadow Showdown

Only one of these silhouettes of Rapunzel matches the bigger picture exactly. Which one is it?

a

b

c

Spot the Difference

There are eight differences between these images of Mulan having dinner with her family. Look closely and see if you can spot them all!

How Many Words?

DAY 109

How many words can you make from the letters in **THE MAGIC CARPET**? In every word you make, you can only use each letter once!

Example: REPEAT

Quote Quiz

DAY 110

Read all of the quotes and see if you can remember which character said them!

1 ......

2 ......

3 ......

4 ......

a Be our guest!

b There may be something there that wasn't there before.

c She's in love with the Beast!

d She'll never see me as anything but a monster.

DAY 111

Mother Maze

Find a way through the maze to help Merida reach her mother, Elinor Bear.

FINISH

START

Culinary Changes

Tiana is busy in the kitchen cooking up some delicious food! Can you find eight differences between the two scenes?

DAY 112

Sea Sketch

Copy this picture of Flounder using the grid to help you!

Once Upon a Time...

In the space below, write a short story about Moana!

Sunflower Sizes

Help Pocahontas to put the sunflowers in the correct height order.
Label them 1 to 7, with 1 being the smallest and 7 being the tallest.

a ....
b ....
c ....
d ....
e ....
f ....
g ....

Lost Property

Follow each line to discover which
button belongs to which mouse!

1

2

3

a

b

c

Castle Colouring

Use your best crayons to decorate this
scene of the Beast carrying Belle's books
through the castle grounds!

DAY
117

What a Mess!

Snow White is tidying the Dwarfs' cottage! How many of each item can you count in the jumble?

a Spoons ....

b Plates ....

c Bowls ....

DAY 118

Odd One Out

Which of the close-ups below is not part of the image of Mulan and Khan?

a
b
c
d
e

DAY 119

Fairy Sudoku

Complete the puzzle by making sure there's only one good fairy in every row and column.

DAY 120

a
b
c
d
e

DAY 121

START

FINISH

Royal Route

Can you help Rapunzel find her way back to her parents? Draw a route through the maze that goes over every flag once, but avoids the towers!

DAY 122

a

b

c

d

e

Monkeying Around!

Look closely at the pictures of Abu and match them to the correct shadows. Which one doesn't have a match?

1

2

3

4

Jigsaw Jumble

Complete the scene by matching where the jigsaw pieces belong in the picture.

a

b

d

c

Merida Makeover

DAY 124

In the space below, draw a brand new outfit for Merida!

DAY 125

Pumpkin Bingo

Cinderella has picked a huge pumpkin from the
pumpkin patch! Which bingo card exactly matches hers?

a

b

c

d

e

DAY 126

A Friend to Nature

Use your crayons to colour this picture
of Pocahontas running through the forest!

Who Said It?

Each one of these quotes was said by one of the characters shown. Do you know who said what?

a There is nowhere you could go that I won't be with you.

b No one goes beyond the reef!

c The ocean chose me.

d I've got your back, chosen one. Go save the world.

1 ......
2 ......
3 ......
4 ......

Seahorse Search

Help Ariel to count how many of each colour seahorse there are swimming in the ocean!

Seahorses to find:

....

Royal Close-ups

Aurora and Prince Phillip are busy planning a party!
Which of the close-ups below isn't part of the scene?

a

b

c

d

e

f

Dwarf Dial

Discover who the mystery Dwarf is by counting every fourth
letter on the dial. Then, write the name in the spaces below.

D _ _ _ _ _ _

START ↘

D L F I O J E F H B W E N S I Y I J D

?

Belle's Books

Which pile contains the most books?
Label the piles 1 to 4, with 1 being the
smallest and 4 being the biggest.

Coordinate Chaos

Cinderella has arrived at the palace! Using the coordinates, write where in the scene you can find everything listed at the bottom of the page.

Example:

a (1, a)

a (___, ___)

b (___, ___)

c (___, ___)

d (___, ___)

e (___, ___)

f (___),(___)

Palace Paths

Help Jasmine and Aladdin escape the palace by finding two paths that equal 20 when added together. Which two paths should they take?

a 1
1
2
b 2 5 3 20 5 3 5 e
1
3
c 2
d 5
1
2
5
4
2
1 f

Spot the Difference

Can you spot the eight differences between these pictures of Rapunzel and Maximus?

DAY 135

Once Upon a Time...

In the space, write a short story about Tiana!
What adventure is she going on today?

DAY 136

Statue Search

How many statues can you find
hiding amongst the shields?
Write your answer in the space
at the bottom of the page.

There are .... statues!

How Many Words?

How many words can you make using the
letters in **DINGLEHOPPER**? In every word you
make, you can only use each letter once!

Example: **HELPER**

_____ _____

_____ _____

_____ _____

_____ _____

Follow the Fans

Following the sequence, find the right path
through the fans that will lead you to Mulan.

Sequence to follow:

START

FINISH

Maurice Maze

Follow the paths to discover which one will lead Belle back to her father, Maurice.

a

b

c

Meeko Masterpiece

Using the grid to help you, draw a picture of Meeko!

DAY
141

Sequence Search

Look closely at the grid and see if you can spot all the sequences shown below.

Example:

a

b

c

d

e

DAY 142

Snow Shadows

Can you work out which is the only shadow that matches the bigger picture of Snow White exactly?

a b c d e

Beach Colouring

Complete this picture of Moana at the beach with Gramma Tala, Pua and Heihei using your colouring pencils!

DAY 143

DAY 144

Stargazers

How many stars are in the sky as Jasmine and Aladdin fly past on the Magic Carpet?

There are .... stars!

DAY 145

Name Scramble

Unscramble the letters below to discover the characters' names. Then, write their names in the spaces below.

a inata _ _ _ _ _ _

b hrcatoetl _ _ _ _ _ _ _ _ _

c vaenne _ _ _ _ _ _

d siulo _ _ _ _ _

e duaroe _ _ _ _ _ _

DAY 146

Clues
1. The real Merida is holding a falcon
2. The real Merida's glove is not black
3. The real Merida has blue eyes

Merida Mix-up

Follow the clues to discover which image is really Merida!

DAY 147

START

Light the Way

Lead Rapunzel to Corona by following the path of lanterns, avoiding the other objects. She must go over every lantern once!

FINISH

Dreams Do Come True

Cinderella now lives in the palace with Prince Charming. In the space below, draw your dream home!

DAY 148

On Their Own

In the grid below, all the Enchanted Servants appear multiple times except for one! Can you find them?

Rowing Route

Pocahontas is rowing to meet her best friend, Nakoma. Which path has the most compasses and will lead her down the best route?

Once Upon a Time...

In the space below, write a story about Mulan!
What adventure is she going on today?

Culinary Colouring

Use your best pencils to colour this picture
of Tiana perfecting her latest recipe.

Forest Friends

Which of the close-ups below doesn't belong in the picture of Snow White and the animals?

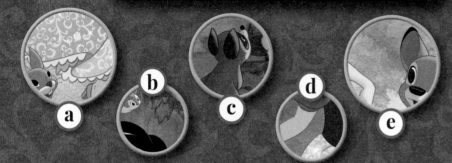

a b c d e

Triplet Trivia

The triplets have written a quiz for you about their sister, Merida! Do you know which statements are true and which are false?

True   False

1. Merida lives in the Scottish Highlands ☐ ☐

2. Merida has blonde hair ☐ ☐

3. Merida's horse is called Andrew ☐ ☐

4. Merida is very good at archery ☐ ☐

5. Merida believes in following your dreams ☐ ☐

Magical Masterpiece

Using the grid as a guide, draw a magnificent picture of Gus in the box on the right.

Set the Scene

Fill the space surrounding Ariel
with a magical underwater scene!

DAY 157

Letter Line

Follow the blue lines to discover who has Maui's magical fish hook! Once you know, write their name below.

START

A	T	W	C	O	Y
T	Y	A	M	T	A	I
M	S	O	A	O	A

T _ _ _ _ _ _

DAY 158

Cushion Chaos

Find and circle which cushion appears only once in the jumble.

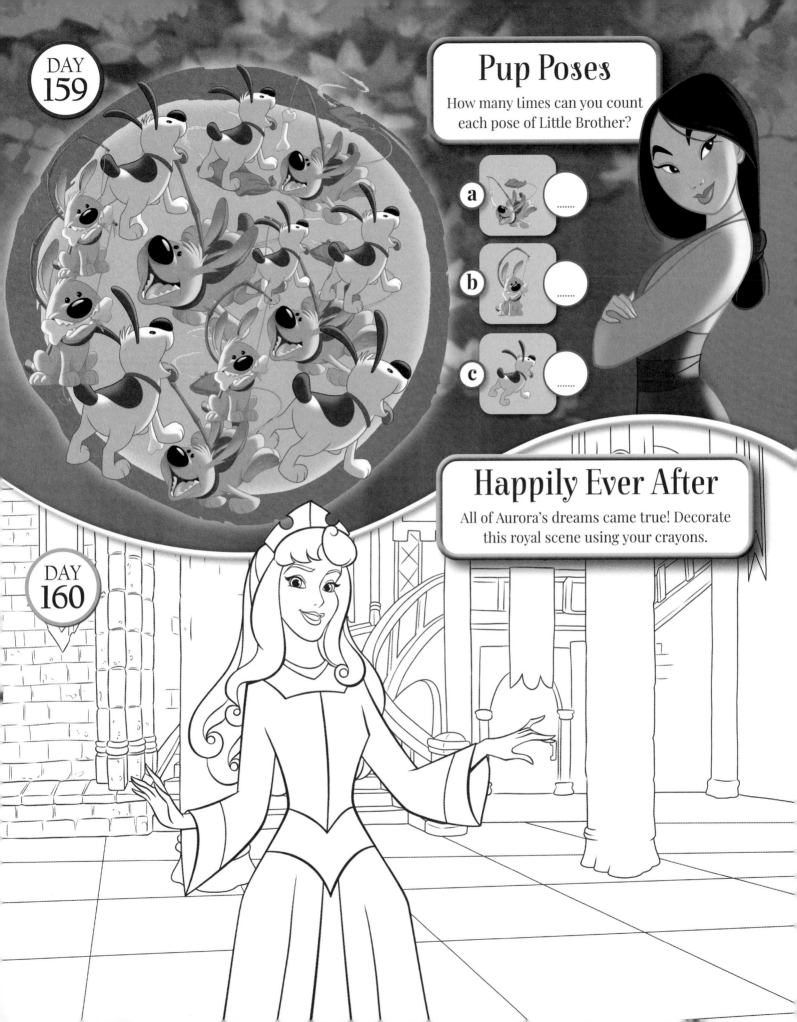

DAY 159

Pup Poses

How many times can you count each pose of Little Brother?

a ....

b ....

c ....

Happily Ever After

All of Aurora's dreams came true! Decorate this royal scene using your crayons.

DAY 160

Cinderella Code

Work out what the secret message says,
using the alphabet code to help you!

Kitchen Clues

Can you find the three items listed below
somewhere in Tiana's kitchen?

1. Green pear
2. Cherry pie
3. Red pepper

Pooch Patterns

Look closely at the sequences and see if you can work out which pose of Max is needed to complete each one.

a

b

c

d

1 ....

2 ....

3 ....

Missing Belle

Which picture of Belle shown below does not have a shadow in the box on the right?

a

b

c

d

e

Scene Changes

One of the smaller pictures of Jasmine is not an
exact match to the bigger picture. Which one is it?

a

b

c

d

e

Noughts and Crosses

Playing with a friend, choose who will be noughts and who will be crosses. Then, take it in turns to fill in a space. The winner is the first person to get three in a row horizontally, vertically or diagonally.

The Missing Piece

Which jigsaw piece will complete the scene of Snow White and the Dwarfs?

a
b
c
d
e
f

Princess Pyramid

Help Aurora to fill in the empty spaces in the pyramid by adding together the numbers in the two boxes immediately below!

4

2   1   2   1

Picture Pieces

This picture of Merida and Angus is in pieces! Can you put it back together by matching the pieces to where they belong in the puzzle?

a

b

d

c

e

Real Rapunzel

Only one of these pictures is really Rapunzel! Follow the clues to discover which one it is.

a

b

c

d

Clues

1. Rapunzel is holding a green book

2. Pascal is not sitting on the table

3. Rapunzel is not holding a pink quill

DAY 171

Castle Colouring

Decorate this picture of Cinderella in the ballroom at the royal castle!

DAY 172

Friend Differences

There are five differences between these pictures of Moana and Maui. Can you spot them all?

Petal Puzzle

Each row and column can only contain a certain amount of roses. Read the numbers, then work out where they should go! Start with the row labelled '4' and add all the roses. Show the empty boxes by putting Xs in them.

	2	2	3	3
3	🌹		🌹	🌹
1	✗			🌹
4		🌹		
2				

Mermaid Mirror

The reflection of the water has turned this message upside down! Place a mirror on the dotted lines to read it, then write what it says.

_ _ _ _
MAKE

_ _ _ _
YOUR

_ _ _ _ _
VOICE

_ _ _ _ _
HEARD

Quick Quiz

How much do you know about *Moana*?
Test yourself with this quick quiz!

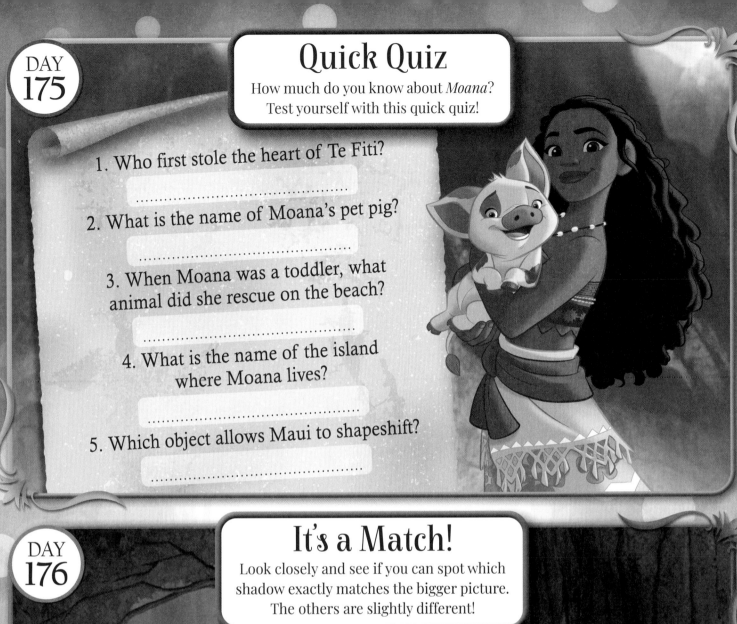

1. Who first stole the heart of Te Fiti?

....

2. What is the name of Moana's pet pig?

....

3. When Moana was a toddler, what animal did she rescue on the beach?

....

4. What is the name of the island where Moana lives?

....

5. Which object allows Maui to shapeshift?

....

It's a Match!

Look closely and see if you can spot which shadow exactly matches the bigger picture. The others are slightly different!

Just One Kiss!

Following an evil curse, Prince Naveen was transformed into a frog! Decorate the scene of him and Tiana using your best pencils.

Powhatan Path

Lead Pocahontas to her father, Chief Powhatan, by finding the path that adds up exactly to 20.

a 2 3 2 1 2

2 3 2 2 1 2

b 1 3 3 2 1 3 ......

2 2 2 2 2 ......

c 3 2 1 1 ......

3 3 2 3 1

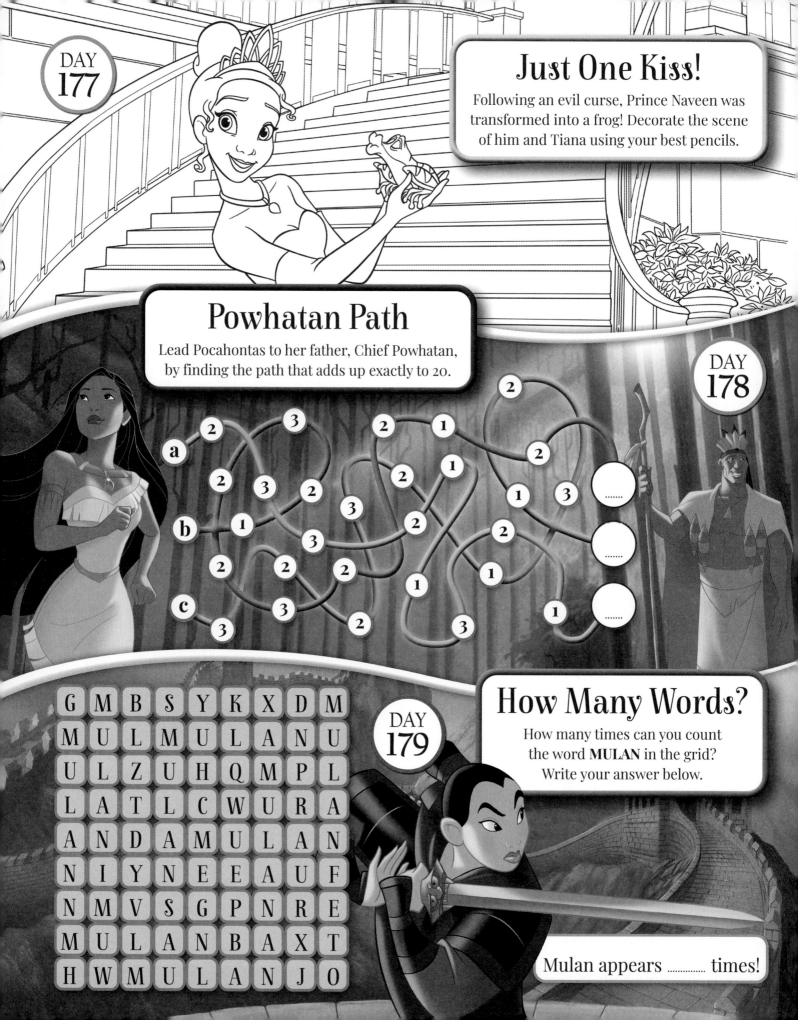

G	M	B	S	Y	K	X	D	M
M	U	L	M	U	L	A	N	U
U	L	Z	U	H	Q	M	P	L
L	A	T	L	C	W	U	R	A
A	N	D	A	M	U	L	A	N
N	I	Y	N	E	E	A	U	F
N	M	V	S	G	P	N	R	E
M	U	L	A	N	B	A	X	T
H	W	M	U	L	A	N	J	O

How Many Words?

How many times can you count the word **MULAN** in the grid? Write your answer below.

Mulan appears .... times!

Cupcake Counter

Rapunzel has lots of cupcakes to make for her friends and family!
Match the lettered boxes to the same sequence below to get a number.
The first one has been done for you. Then, add all the numbers
together to get a total number of cupcakes needed.

Total cupcakes ....

Pet Portrait

Using the image on the left to help you, draw a picture of Jasmine's tiger, Rajah!

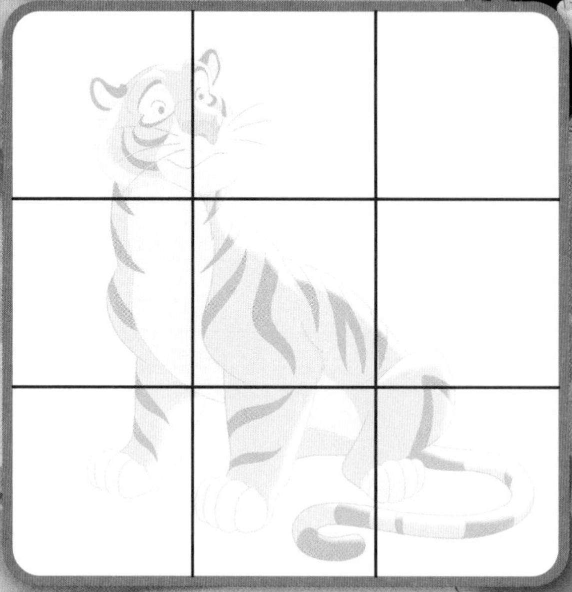

Pattern Pals

Help Cinderella to complete these sequences of her mouse friends by filling in the empty spaces!

1

2

3

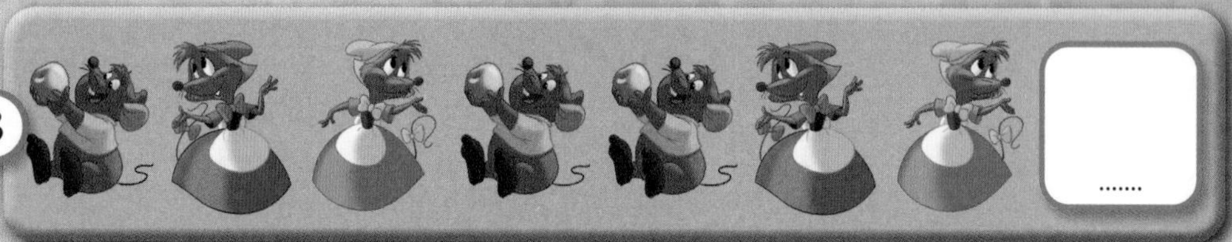

a

b

c

d

Hit the Bullseye!

Which sum equals 32 and will help Merida to hit the bullseye?

32

a 5 x 6 = ... **b** 3 x 11 = ...

c 4 x 8 = ... **d** 4 x 7 = ...

Who Said That?

Do you remember who said the quotes below? Match them to who said it!

1 ....

2 ....

3 ....

4 ....

a Make it pink!

b Now, come have a nice cup of tea, dear. I'm sure it'll work out somehow.

c Oh no, not pink. Make it blue!

d But don't you remember? We've met before.

Mermaid Makeover

Ariel has just arrived on land! In the space below, draw an outfit for her to wear.

Chase your Dreams

Tiana always dreamed of opening her own restaurant. Help her get there by finding a route through the maze that avoids all the glass bottles.

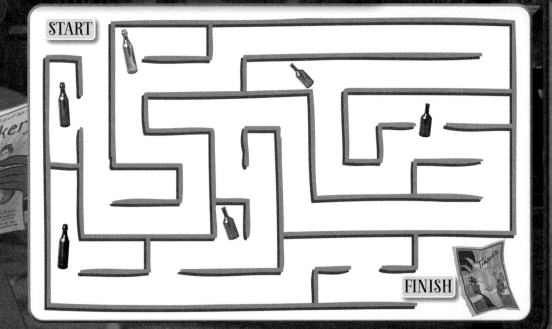

Compass Clutter

DAY 187

Which of the compasses shown in the box appears only once in the jumble?

a b c
d e

Dot-to-Dot

DAY 188

Complete this dot-to-dot of Chip. Then, colour him in!

Beautiful Beach

Little Moana loves the ocean! Complete the picture
by drawing a beach scene around her.

Tangle of Wisps

How many of each will o' the wisp is in the jumble? Write your answers in the boxes.

a   **b**   **c**

....

Diamond Dash

Help the Dwarfs find a path from start to finish by only moving to diamonds that share one of their two colours.

FINISH

Pascal Picture

Draw and colour a picture of Pascal, using the grid to help you!

A Special Story

In the space below, write a
magical story about Cinderella!

Path of a Princess

Jasmine is making her way out of the palace to
meet Aladdin! Find a path that goes over every
empty square only once, but avoids the guards.

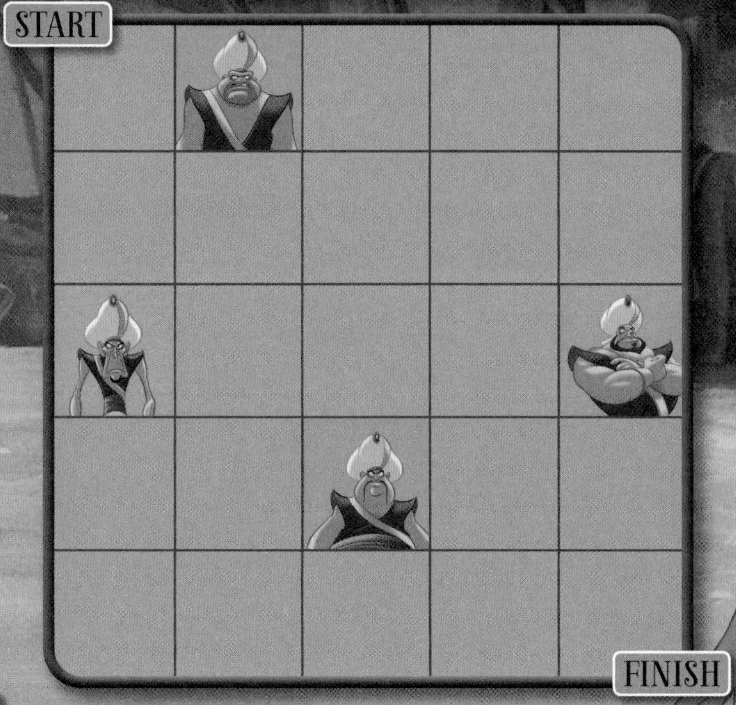

START

FINISH

Mushu Maze

DAY 195

Help Mulan and Khan get to Mushu by marking the squares that the dragon cannons are occupying. Then, find a route through the maze that avoids them!

	1	2	3	4	5	6
A						START
B						
C						
D						
E						
F						FINISH

(d,2) (e,1) (b,2)

(d,5) (e,5)

DAY 196

Royal Celebrations

There are six differences between these scenes! Look closely and see if you can spot them all.

DAY 197

Perfect Pyramid

Can you complete this number pyramid? Fill in the empty spaces by adding together the two numbers directly below.

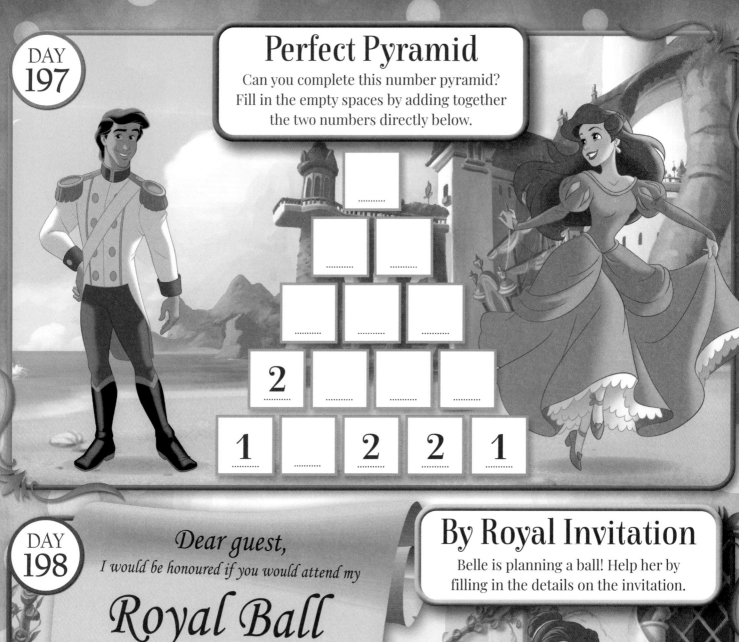

....				
....	....			
....	....	....		
2	....	....	....	
1	....	2	2	1

DAY 198

By Royal Invitation

Belle is planning a ball! Help her by filling in the details on the invitation.

Dear guest,

I would be honoured if you would attend my

Royal Ball

It will be held at:

....

(Think of an enchanting venue)

The date will be:

....

(What day of the week will it be?)

The dress code is:

....

(What should guests wear?)

Please RSVP to Princess Belle

Pocahontas Picture
Use your crayons to colour the scene!

Bird Bubble
Only one bubble contains all the birds shown in the box below. Can you work out which one?

Birds to find:

Silhouette Sorter

Tiana needs your help to match the silhouettes of Ray to the correct pictures! Draw lines to show your answers.

a b c

d e

1 2 5 3 4

Moana Message

Using the alphabet to help you, can you work out what Moana's message says? Write it in the spaces below!

a b c d e f g h i j k

l m n o p q r s t

u v w x y z

__ __   __ __ __ __   __ __ __ __ __ __ __ __ __

Food Favourites

Which item of food do Merida's family like the most? Follow the paths to find out!

1

2

3

a

b

c

Magic Carpet Ride

Jasmine and Abu are riding on the Magic Carpet.
In the background, draw the city of Agrabah.

DAY
205

Forest Finds

Aurora is busy picking berries with her animal friends in the forest. How many of each image can you find in the scene?

a ...... Berries

b ...... Squirrels

c ...... Rabbits

d ...... Bluebirds

Which Wool?

Look closely and see if you can spot which basket of wool is exactly the same as the bigger picture.

DAY
206

a

b

c

d

e

f

DAY 207

1. When Mulan was in the army what name did she go by?

....

2. Whose place did Mulan take in the army?

....

3. What is the name of Mulan's cricket?

....

4. In which city did Mulan defeat Shan Yu?

....

5. What animal is Khan?

....

DAY 208

Best Day Ever!
Connect the dots to complete this picture of Rapunzel leaving the tower for the first time. Then, colour the scene!

DAY 209

Scene Setter

Where is Pocahontas? You decide! Use your pencils and crayons to create a scene around her.

DAY 210

Merida Match

Can you complete this picture of Merida by correctly matching the pieces below to where they belong?

a

b

c

d

e

f

On Their Own

In the grid, all of the Dwarfs appear multiple times... except for one! Can you spot him?

Dinner Differences

Look closely at this picture of Ariel making dinner and see if you can spot all eight differences!

Roll and Race

Playing with a friend, see who can get to the
finish first! Place your counters or coins on 'Start', then
take it in turns to roll the dice. If you roll an even number,
move forward one space. If you roll an odd number,
stay where you are until you roll again.

You will need:

Counters
or coins

A dice

FINISH	FINISH
4	4
3	3
2	2
1	1
START	START

Who Said It?

Match the quotes to the characters who said them by writing the correct letters in the empty boxes.

DAY 214

a Let's make some magic!

b If I do marry, I want it to be for love.

c From this day forth, the princess shall marry whoever she deems worthy.

d I'm not worthless. And I don't have fleas!

1 ......

2 ......

3 ......

4 ......

The Missing Piece

DAY 215

Which jigsaw piece completes the picture of Cinderella arriving at the royal ball?

a

b

c

d

e

f

Ready or Not, Here I Come!

DAY 216

Belle is playing hide-and-seek with Chip! Draw a path through the maze to help her find him.

FINISH

START

DAY 217

Shopping Search

Tiana has a shopping list of all the ingredients she needs to make her next dish. Look closely in the jumble and tick the items off as you find them!

3 bananas ○

1 pumpkin ○

4 bunches of grapes ○

5 tomatoes ○

Letter Line

Follow the purple lines to discover who Aurora is looking for! Once you know, write their name below.

START

A	X	W	C	F	Y
T	Y	E	U	A	R	I
Z	Z	A	N	B	O	D

F ___ ___ ___ ___

DAY 218

Once Upon a Time...

Rapunzel loves to explore! Where is she going today? Write a short story in the space below.

_____

_____

_____

_____

_____

_____

_____

_____

Scene It All

Look closely at the scene on the left, then cover it and see if you can answer the questions below!

Questions

1. What colour is Mulan's paint brush?

....

2. Is Mushu in the scene?

....

3. Are the flowers in the vase purple?

....

4. Are there any extra paint brushes?

....

5. How many cushions are there?

....

Cottage Coordinates

DAY 221

Merida has arrived at the Witch's Cottage. Using coordinates, can you answer all of the questions on the right?

a
b
c

1 2 3 4 5

Questions

1. In which square is the witch?
   Example: **(3,b)**
   ....

2. What animals can you see in square **(1,b)**?
   ....

3. How many squares contain barrels?
   ....

4. How many will o' the wisps are in square **(5,a)**?
   ....

5. In which square are Merida's arrows?
   ....

Forest Friends

DAY 222

Bring this scene of Snow White and her friends to life by adding lots of colour!

Missing Genie

Look at the boxes below and see if you can work
out which one is missing a picture of the Genie!

a

b

c

d

Dots and Boxes

Playing with a friend or family member, take it in turns to draw a line
between two dots. If your line completes a box, write your initial inside it.
The winner is the person with the most boxes when the grid is full!

Lost Letters

Can you fill in the empty spaces to complete the character names?

L_MI_R_
_OG_WO__H
MA__R_C
T_E _EAS_
MR_ _ _O_T_
_AST__

Maui Maze

Maui needs your help so he can shapeshift! Find a path through the maze, making sure to collect his fish hook on the way.

FINISH

START

a b c

Odd One Out

Which of these images of Rapunzel and her friends is slightly different and therefore the odd one out?

The Race Home

Mulan is on her way home from the Imperial City to see her father. Help her to find a route through the maze, but watch out for the broken paths – you can't pass there!

START

FINISH

Picture Pieces

Tiana loves seeing her friends enjoying her food! Put the scene back in the right order by labelling the pieces from 1 to 5.

a ....
b ....
c ....
d ....
e ....

Treasure Trove

Circle the piece of treasure in Ariel's grotto that only appears once!

DAY 231

Love Will Always Find a Way

Aurora and Phillip are dancing across the ballroom! Complete the scene with your best crayons.

DAY 232

Slipper Search

Which path contains glass slippers that are all the same colour?

a

b

c

d

DAY 233

Love Note

Pocahontas has left a note for John Smith. Work out what the secret message says by using the alphabet code to help you!

a b c d e f g h i j k l m

n o p q r s t u v w x y z

_____ , _____

_____ _____ _____

DAY 234

Palace Path

Draw a route through the maze that will guide Jasmine back to the palace.

FINISH

START

DAY 235

Party Prep

Belle is preparing a tea party! She needs five red roses to decorate each table. Count the flowers and work out how many tables she can decorate.

Number of roses:
....

Number of tables:
....

DAY 236

Terrific Tartan

Using the patterns on the right for inspiration, design your own tartan below!

Snow Story

Fill the space below with a wonderful tale about Snow White and the Dwarfs.

Once upon a time...

_____

_____

_____

_____

_____

_____

_____

_____

_____

_____

_____

_____

The End

Mulan Colouring

Decorate this action pose of Mulan!

Mirror Message

This message has been flipped! Place a mirror on the dotted lines to find out what it says. Write the answer in the spaces.

SOMETIMES

OUR STRENGTHS

LIE BENEATH

THE SURFACE

Perfect Pal

Only one of these pictures of Flounder exactly matches the bigger picture. Look closely and see if you can spot which one.

a

b

c

d

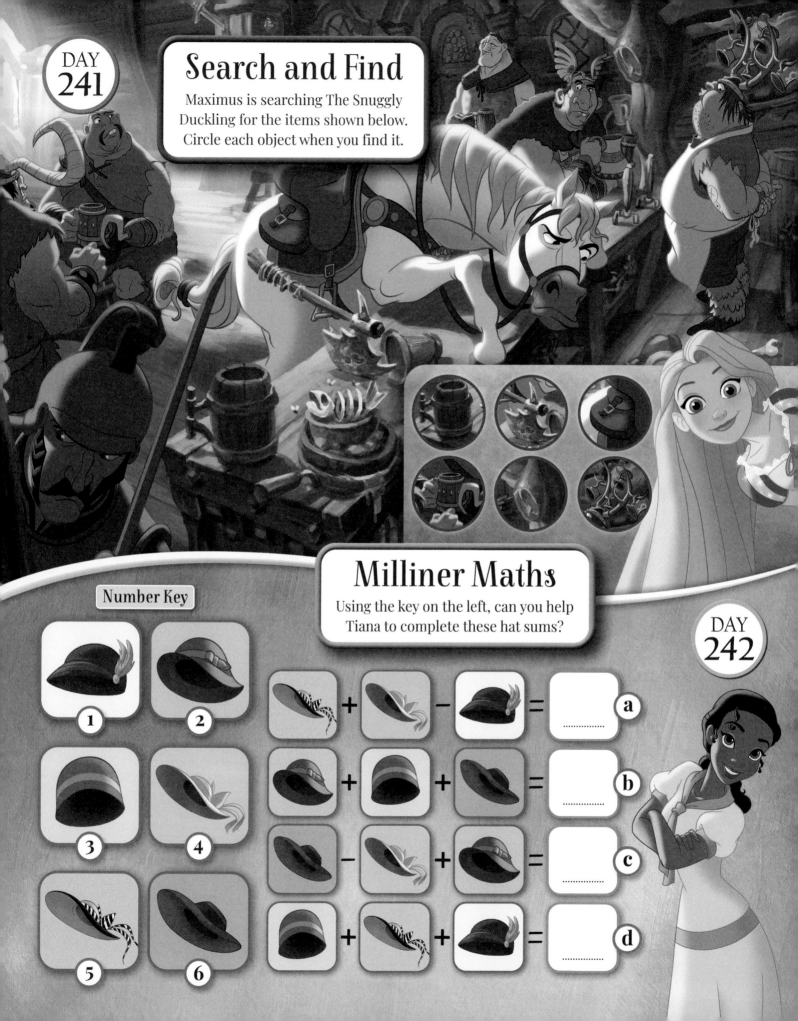

Search and Find

Maximus is searching The Snuggly Duckling for the items shown below. Circle each object when you find it.

Milliner Maths

Using the key on the left, can you help Tiana to complete these hat sums?

Number Key

1

2

3

4

5

6

a ....

b ....

c ....

d ....

DAY 243

Birthday Girl

Aurora's aunts are having a bit of trouble with her birthday cake. Decorate an amazing cake for Aurora.

Escape Route

Help Cinderella to find a way to her Fairy Godmother, making sure she goes over every empty square once, but avoids her stepmother and stepsisters.

DAY 244

START

FINISH

DAY 245

Scene It!

One of the smaller scenes is slightly different to the bigger picture. Look closely and see if you can spot which one!

a   b
c   d

DAY 246

Nuisance Napkins

In the jumble of napkins, every colour appears multiple times except one! Can you spot it?

The .... napkin only appears once!

DAY 247

Merida Masterpiece

Use your best colouring pencils to decorate this scene of Merida!

DAY 248

Pocahontas Paths

Discover the name of Pocahontas' best friend by following the paths and writing the letters in the boxes.

K M N A A O

Wish List

DAY 249

The Genie grants his master three wishes! What would you wish for?

1 ....

2 ....

3 ....

True Shadow

DAY 250

Only one of these shadows exactly matches the bigger picture of Mulan and Mushu. Can you spot which one?

a   b   c   d

Who Said That?

DAY 251

Think you know Tiana and her friends? Read each of the quotes and match them to the character who said it!

1 ......

2 ......

3 ......

4 ......

5 ......

a I wanna be human too so I could play jazz with the big boys!

b I was beginnin' to think that wishin' on stars was for babies...

c A bug gotta do what a bug gotta do!

d My dream wouldn't be complete without you in it.

e Achidanza!

Snow's Search

Snow White is looking for Dopey. Find a path
through the maze that will lead her to him.

START

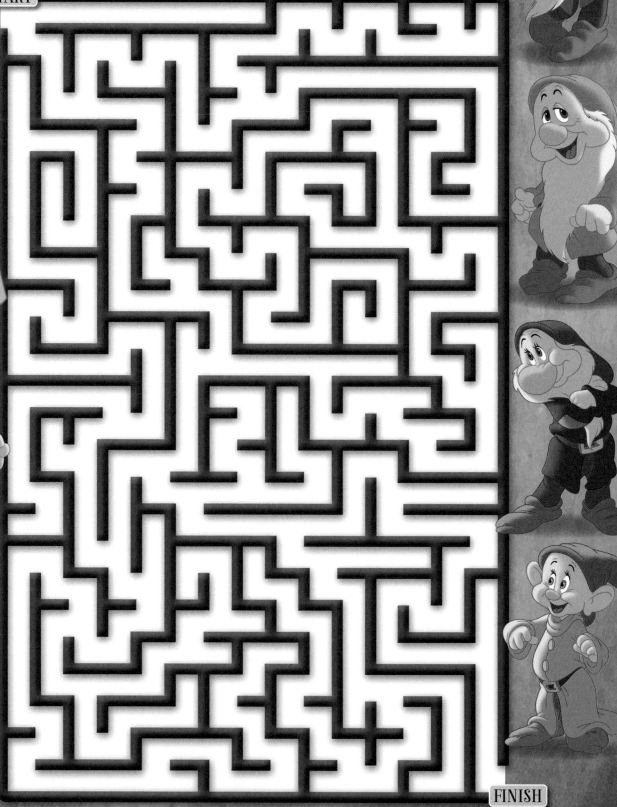

FINISH

Pretty Pairs

Can you find all of the pairs in the grid below?
Draw lines between them to show your answers.

Wardrobe Way

Cinderella isn't sure what to wear
today! Find the path with the most
bows to help her decide.

a

b

c

Outfit 1

Outfit 2

Outfit 3

Family Frame

In the frame, draw a lovely picture of you and your family.

Perfect Picture

Look at the close-ups and work out where each of them belongs in the scene!

a

b

c

d

e

Counting Corn

Each of the boxes below must contain ten cobs of corn.
Count how many there are, then write in the empty boxes
how many more cobs of corn are needed to make ten.

a) ....

b) ....

c) ....

d) ....

Musical Masterpiece

Tiana and Louis love jazz music! Use your
best pencils to colour the scene.

Song Sequences

DAY 259

Help Ariel to complete these song sheets by following the sequences and filling in the empty boxes so she knows what comes next.

a

b

c

1 2 3 4 5

How Many Times?

DAY 260

How many times can you find the word **MERIDA** in the grid below?

Merida appears .... times!

J	M	E	R	I	D	A	M	A
M	E	R	I	D	A	F	E	D
R	R	L	C	I	R	M	R	I
I	I	T	P	D	M	A	I	R
L	D	O	G	R	S	F	D	E
N	A	M	E	R	I	D	A	M

Suits You

The Beast needs a new outfit for when he dances
with Belle. Use the space below to design one for him.

Snow Scene

Look closely at the scene on the right, then cover it and answer the questions below!

1 Is Grumpy in the scene? ....

2 What colour is the Prince's cape? ....

3 How many birds are in the scene? ....

Silly Shapes

Can you work out which four pieces below will fit perfectly into the picture of Rapunzel, Flynn and Maximus?

a

b

c

d

e

f

....

....

....

....

Odd One Out

Which picture of Mulan is slightly different to the others?

a

b

c

Colour by Numbers

DAY 265

Using the colour code, decorate these pictures of the good fairies.

Monkey Mayhem

DAY 266

Every picture of Abu has an exact match... except one! Can you find the odd one out?

a   b   c

d   e   f   g

h   i   j   k

START

FINISH

Find Your Way

Help Moana through the maze by finding a route that will lead to her sailboat.

Memory Muddle

Look very closely at Jumble 1, then cover it and see if you can work out which item has been removed in Jumble 2.

Jumble 1

Jumble 2

Badge Blunder

DAY 269

In the jumble below, there is one badge that isn't the same as all the others. Can you see it?

Musical Mermaids

DAY 270

Sebastian needs one of Ariel's sisters to sing in a concert. Match his musical notes to theirs to discover who gets the solo!

a

b

c

d

e

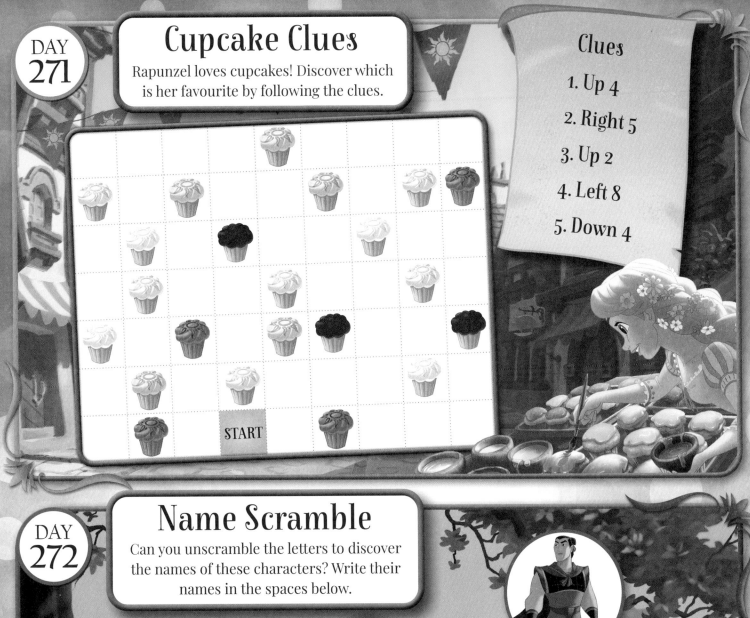

Cupcake Clues

Rapunzel loves cupcakes! Discover which is her favourite by following the clues.

START

Clues

1. Up 4
2. Right 5
3. Up 2
4. Left 8
5. Down 4

Name Scramble

Can you unscramble the letters to discover the names of these characters? Write their names in the spaces below.

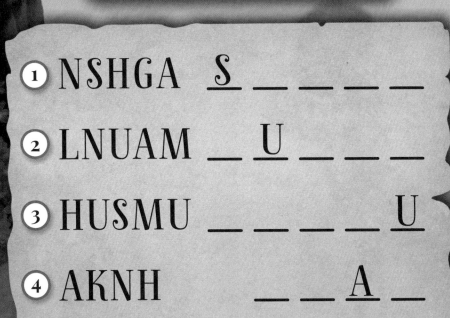

① NSHGA S _ _ _ _

② LNUAM _ U _ _ _

③ HUSMU _ _ _ _ _ U

④ AKNH _ _ A _

DAY 271

DAY 272

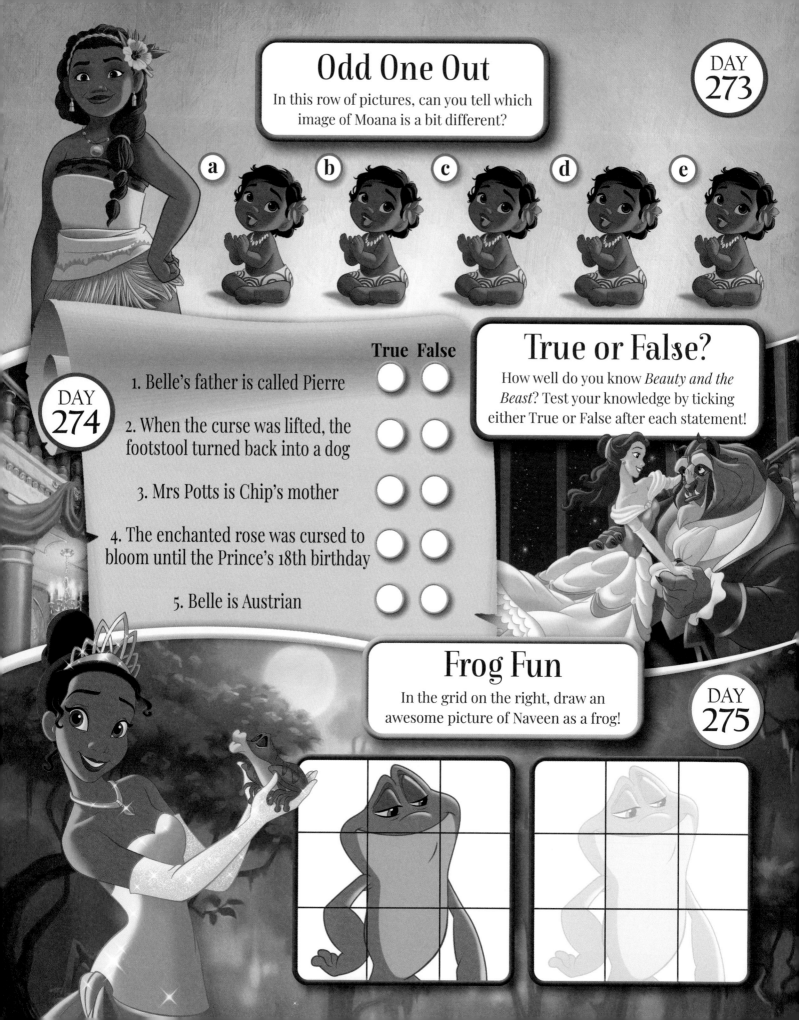

Odd One Out

In this row of pictures, can you tell which image of Moana is a bit different?

a b c d e

	True	False
1. Belle's father is called Pierre	◯	◯
2. When the curse was lifted, the footstool turned back into a dog	◯	◯
3. Mrs Potts is Chip's mother	◯	◯
4. The enchanted rose was cursed to bloom until the Prince's 18th birthday	◯	◯
5. Belle is Austrian	◯	◯

True or False?

How well do you know *Beauty and the Beast*? Test your knowledge by ticking either True or False after each statement!

Frog Fun

In the grid on the right, draw an awesome picture of Naveen as a frog!

Pocahontas Poses

Pocahontas loves everything about nature.
Which box is missing a picture of her?

Magical Moment

Jasmine is flying over Agrabah on the Magic Carpet.
Colour the scene using your best pencils!

How Many Words?

How many words can you make out of the letters
in **FAIRY GODMOTHER**? For every word you
make, you can only use each letter once.

Example: **DREAMT**

DAY
279

A Real Princess

Only one of the pictures is really of Snow White. Follow the clues below to find out which one.

a **b** **c**

d **e** **f**

Clues

1. Snow White is wearing a red headband
2. There is not a bucket next to Snow White
3. Snow White is holding a bluebird
4. Snow White has a bow on her shoe
5. Snow White is not wearing a blue cape

Character Counter

In the grid below, which character appears the most amount of times?

DAY
280

Sword Sums

Using the number key to help you,
complete these sword sums!

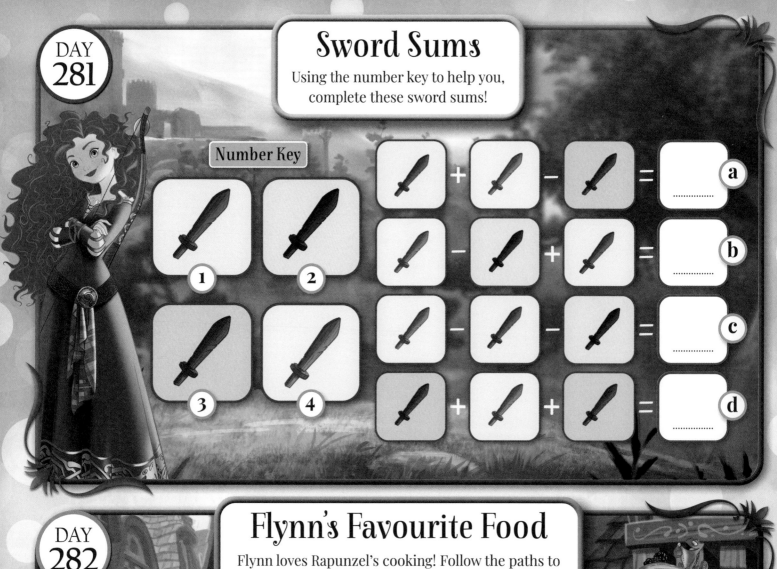

Number Key

a

b

c

d

Flynn's Favourite Food

Flynn loves Rapunzel's cooking! Follow the paths to
find out which will lead him to her... and breakfast!

Close-up Chaos

DAY 283

Each of the close-ups belong in one of the scenes.
Write the correct letters in the empty boxes.

a

b

c

d

1 ......

...... 2

3 ......

...... 4

Dog Drawing

DAY 284

Draw a picture of Little Brother, using the
grid as a guide. Then, colour him in!

Once Upon a Time...

Ariel and Flounder love exploring underwater.
Write about their latest adventure below!

Once upon a time...

_____

_____

_____

_____

_____

_____

_____

_____

_____

_____

_____

The End

DAY 286

Domino Dash

Help Pocahontas to complete the path of dominoes by matching the pieces to the correct spaces.

START

a

b

c

FINISH

1

2

3

DAY 287

Save Snow White

The Dwarfs need to save Snow White from the Evil Queen! Which of the smaller formations fits perfectly around the silhouettes of the Evil Queen so she's surrounded?

a

b

c

Movie Moments

In which order did these infamous moments happen? Label them 1 to 4, 1 being first and 4 being last.

DAY 288

a

b

c

d

Star Search

Ray loves Evangeline, the evening star. Find a route through the maze that will lead him to his love.

FINISH

START

Quick Quiz

Read and answer the questions to see how well you know *Cinderella*!

1. What is the name of Cinderella's horse?

....

2. Finish the magic words: Bibbidi-bobbidi...?

....

3. Who delivered the invitation for the Royal Ball to Cinderella's home?

....

4. What are Cinderella's stepsisters called?

....

5. What animal is Jaq?

....

Close-up Royalty

Can you tell where the close-ups should go in the scene?
One of them doesn't belong. See if you can find it!

1

2 ....

3 ....

4 ....

5 ....

a

b

c

d

e

f

Turtle Rescue!

Colour in this adorable picture of little
Moana rescuing a baby turtle on the beach.

DAY 293

Castle Code

Mrs Potts has a message for Belle! Use the alphabet code below to discover what it says.

a b c d e f g h i j k

l m n o p q r s t

u v w x y z

_____ _____ _____ _____ _____

DAY 294

Perfect Portrait

In the space below, draw a self-portrait!

295

Frame Finder

Look closely at the frames below and circle where they are in the scene!

DAY 296

Shell Stacker

Help Ariel and Flounder to complete the box of shells by working out which pieces fit perfectly to fill the space.

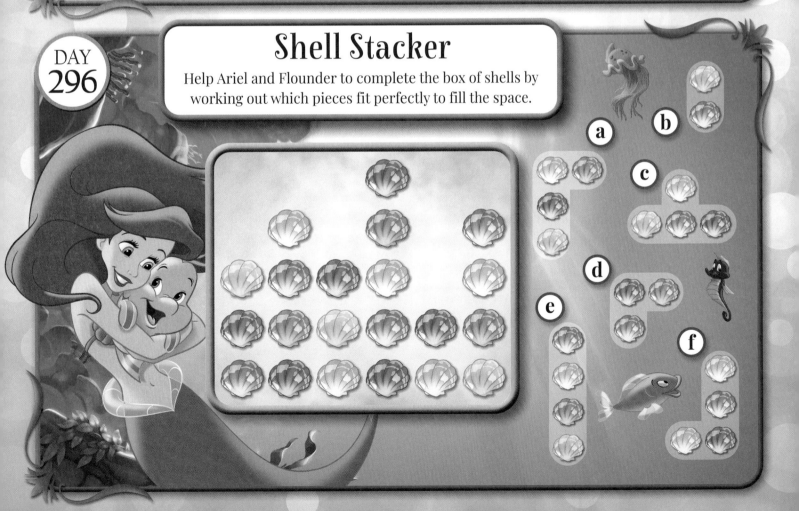

a b c d e f

Attack of the Pirates!

How many times can you find the pose below in the jumble of Kakamora?

appears

....

times!

Odd One Out

Look closely at these silhouettes and see if you can work out which is slightly different from the others.

a   **b**   **c**

Perfect Setting

Can you match the Agrabah scenes to the captions? Write your answers in the empty spaces!

a The Palace Gardens

b Agrabah Market   **c** Jasmine's Bedroom

d The Sultan's Palace   **e** The Palace Fountain

1 ....   **2** ....   **3** ....   **4** ....   **5** ....

DAY
300

Magical Mazes

Help Aurora and the good fairies
to complete these mazes!

START

FINISH

FINISH

START

START

FINISH

Who Said That?

How well do you know *Pocahontas*? Match the quotes to who you think said them!

a I should be wallowing in riches by now!

b No matter what happens to me, I'll always be with you.

c London? Is that your village?

d You must choose your own path.

e You can tell me. I promise I won't tell anyone.

1 ......

2 ......

3 ......

4 ......

5 ......

Dwarf Decoration

Use your best pencils to colour the Seven Dwarfs.

DAY 302

True Shoes

Help Cinderella to sort her glass slipper collection! Only two of the shoes exactly match the slipper below.

Slippers that match:

○ .... ○ ....

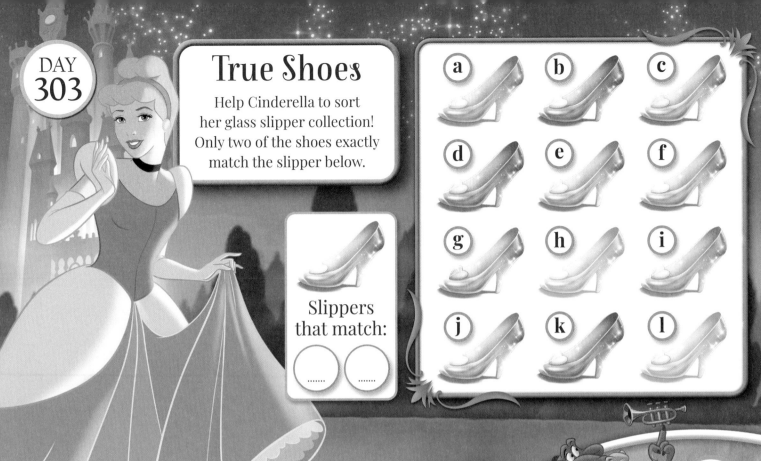

a b c
d e f
g h i
j k l

Spot the Difference

Tiana and Naveen are out shopping for ingredients. Look closely and see if you can spot all eight differences.

Picture Jumble

DAY 305

Help Heihei and Pua to put this picture of Moana back in the right order by labelling the pieces from 1 to 5.

a **b** **c** **d** **e**

Reading Route

DAY 306

Find a route through the books from Cogsworth to Belle by following the key below.

START→

FINISH

KEY

→ ↓ ← ↑

Time for Tea

Only one bubble contains all of the teapots shown below. Can you find which one?

a b c d e f

Teapots to find:

Firework Finds

How many of each firework can you count in the jumble? Write your answers in the spaces.

DAY 307

DAY 308

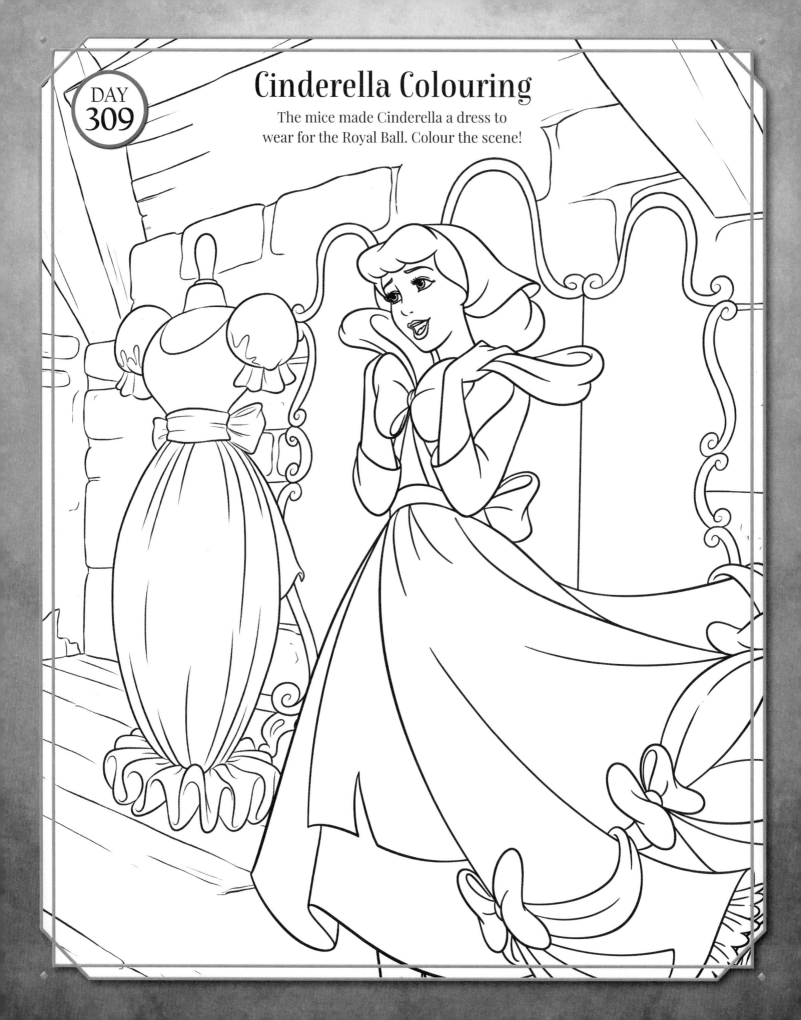

Cinderella Colouring

The mice made Cinderella a dress to
wear for the Royal Ball. Colour the scene!

DAY
309

Treasure Hunt

Find a route that will lead Ariel to the human treasure!

DAY 310

FINISH

START

DAY 311

Perfect Puzzle

Complete Merida's sudoku puzzle by ensuring there is only one of each icon in every column and row!

1 2 3 4

2 3 1

4

3 1

1 2

Letter Lines

Follow the lines to discover a name of one of the Pub Thugs.

DAY 312

A I V I L D M R

Pocahontas Patterns

Which icon is missing in each pattern? Fill in the empty boxes to complete them.

1

2

3

a

b

c

d

Charlotte Clues

Just one of these images is really of Tiana's best friend, Charlotte. Follow the clues to discover which one.

a

b

c

d

Clues

1. Charlotte's gloves are pink

2. Charlotte is wearing a necklace

3. Charlotte is holding a wand

Once Upon a Time...

Write a magical story about Aurora in the space! Be as imaginative as you can.

Royal Route

Help Snow White get to the Prince by working out where the pieces go to complete the path.

START

FINISH

1 ....

2 ....

3 ....

4 ....

a

b

c

d

True or False?

How well do you know *Tangled*? Test your knowledge by
ticking either True or False after each statement!

True   False

1. Rapunzel's pet chameleon
is called Pascal ○ ○

2. Rapunzel's parents are bakers ○ ○

3. Flynn's real name is Henry ○ ○

4. Rapunzel was led home by
following the floating lanterns ○ ○

5. When Rapunzel's magic hair
is cut, it turns red ○ ○

Memorable Scene

Spend time looking around Jasmine's
bedroom, then cover the scene and
answer the questions below.

Questions

1. Is there a mirror in the room?

....

2. How many trunks are there?

....

3. What colour are Jasmine's
trousers?

....

4. Is the magic lamp in Jasmine's
bedroom?

....

Number Paths

DAY 319

Help Mulan by finding two paths that equal 20 when added together. Which two paths should she take?

Perfect Pearl

DAY 320

Discover which pearl belongs to Ariel by following the clues below.

Clues
1. Move up two spaces
2. Move left one space
3. Move up one space
4. Move left three spaces
5. Move down two spaces
6. Move right three spaces

START

How Many Words?

How many words can you make from the letters in **TIANA'S PALACE**? For every word you make, you can only use each letter once!

Example: PENCIL

DAY 321

DAY 322

Castle Colouring

Decorate this scene of Belle, Lumiere and Cogsworth in the castle.

Pocahontas Pictures

One of these pictures of Pocahontas is slightly different. Can you spot which one?

DAY 323

a   b   c   d

Sequence Search

Look closely at the grid and see if you can spot all the sequences shown below.

Example:

a

b

c

d

e

Mother Maze

Find a route that will lead Moana to her mother,
but be careful of the gaps... you can't pass there!

START

FINISH

Quick Quiz

Read the questions and see
how well you know *Snow White
and the Seven Dwarfs*!

1. Two of the Dwarfs' names start with
the letter D. Can you name them?

....

2. Who does the Evil Queen order to
take Snow White into the forest?

....

3. What do the Dwarfs dig for at the mine?

....

4. What meal does Snow White make when
she first arrives at the Dwarfs' cottage?

....

5. Who breaks the spell and wakes Snow White?

....

A Perfect Match

Only one of these pictures of Cinderella and Prince Charming is identical to the bigger picture. Look closely and see if you can find which one!

a

b

c

d

Castle Coordinates

Aurora now lives happily in the castle. Using coordinates, can you answer all of the questions on the right?

a

b

c

1 2 3 4 5

Questions

1. In which square is Merryweather?

Example: **(4,a)**

....

2. In which square is Fauna?

....

3. In which square is Flora?

....

4. What is in square (5,a)?

....

5. In which square is Aurora's crown?

....

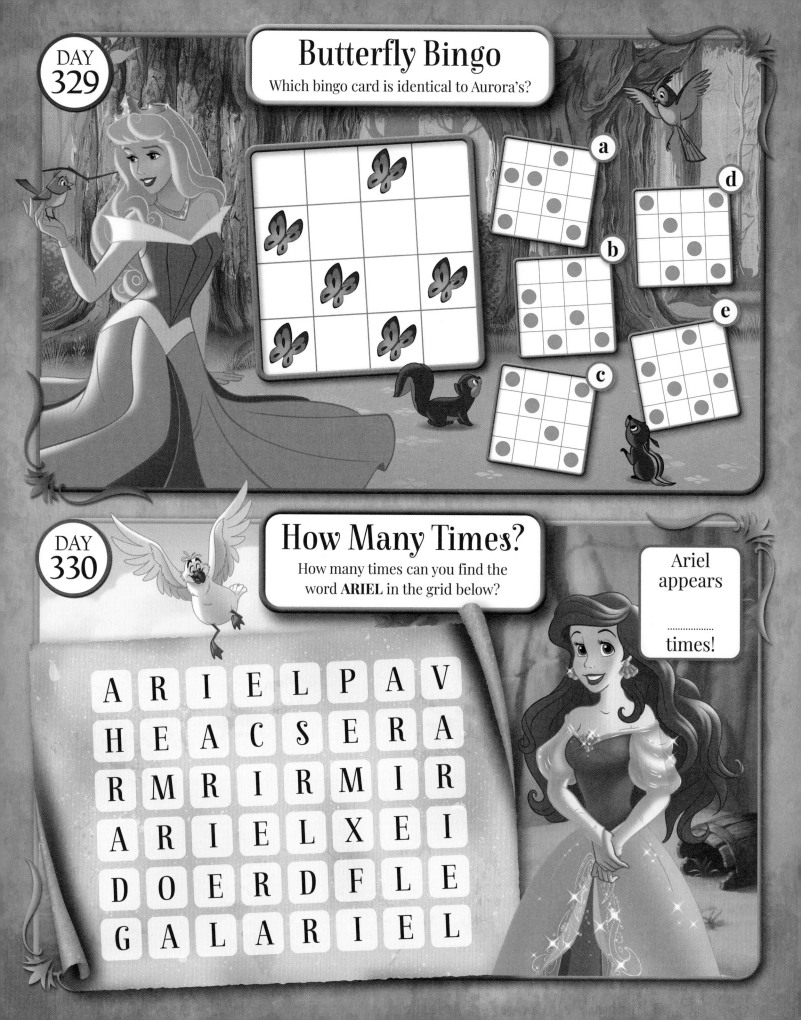

DAY 329

Butterfly Bingo
Which bingo card is identical to Aurora's?

a
b
c
d
e

DAY 330

How Many Times?
How many times can you find the word **ARIEL** in the grid below?

Ariel appears .... times!

A	R	I	E	L	P	A	V
H	E	A	C	S	E	R	A
R	M	R	I	R	M	I	R
A	R	I	E	L	X	E	I
D	O	E	R	D	F	L	E
G	A	L	A	R	I	E	L

Belle Maze

DAY 331

The Beast is looking for Belle!
Find a route through the mazc
that will lead him to her.

FINISH

START

Princess Pottery

DAY 332

Jasmine needs to sort out this jumble of pottery!
How many of each item can you count?

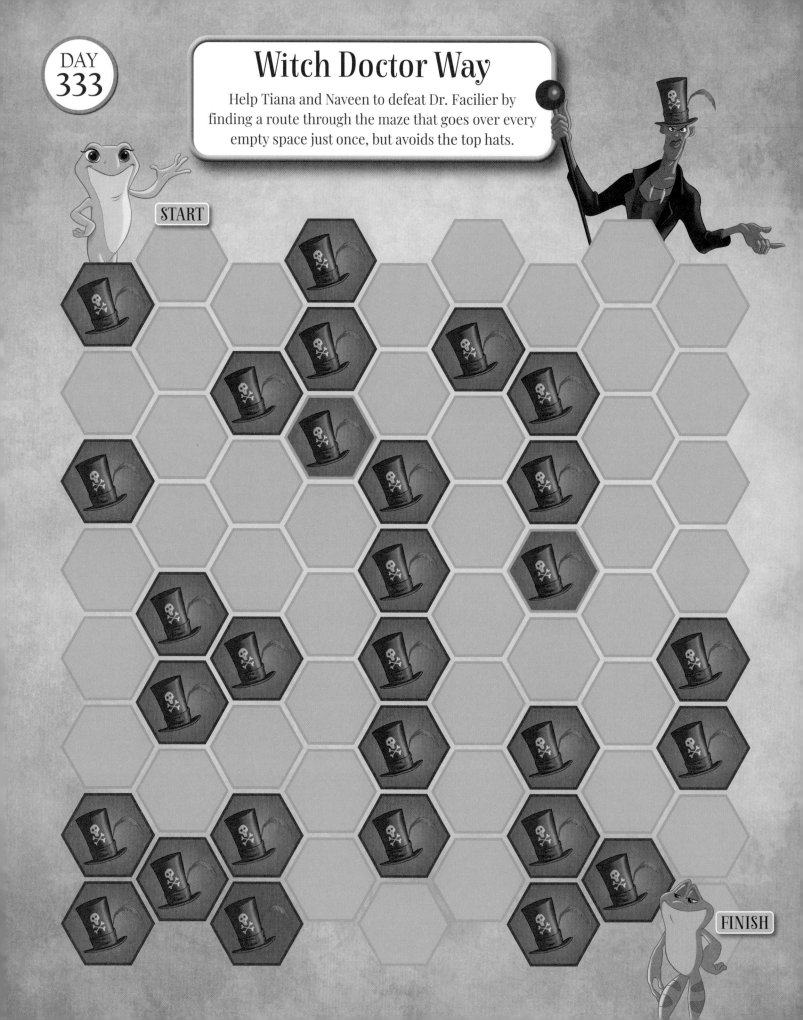

Witch Doctor Way

Help Tiana and Naveen to defeat Dr. Facilier by finding a route through the maze that goes over every empty space just once, but avoids the top hats.

DAY 333

START

FINISH

Cooking Colouring

Mushu and Cri-Kee are cooking!
Colour them in to complete the picture.

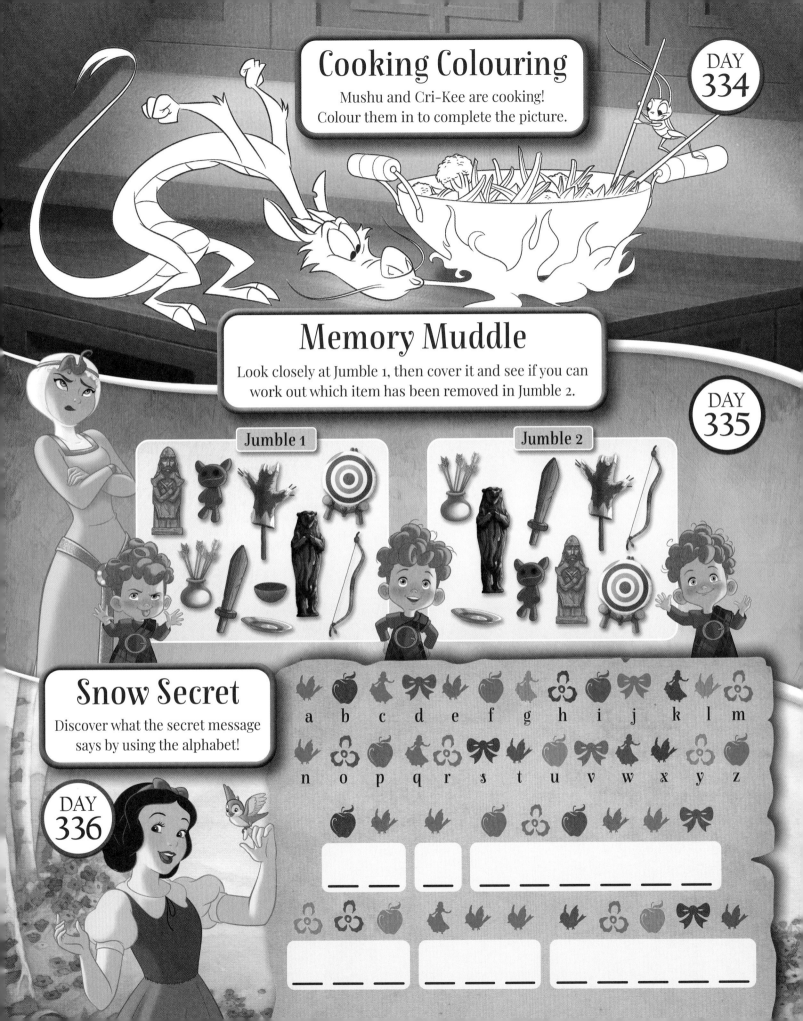

DAY 334

Memory Muddle

Look closely at Jumble 1, then cover it and see if you can
work out which item has been removed in Jumble 2.

DAY 335

Jumble 1

Jumble 2

Snow Secret

Discover what the secret message
says by using the alphabet!

a b c d e f g h i j k l m

n o p q r s t u v w x y z

DAY 336

___ ___   ___   ___ ___ ___ ___ ___ ___ ___

___ ___ ___   ___ ___ ___ ___   ___ ___ ___ ___ ___ ___

Shoe Designer

In the space below, design your own shoe.
Let your imagination run wild!

Nature Numbers

Using the number key, can you help
Pocahontas to complete these sums?

Number Key

1
2
3
4
5
6

a

b

c

d

DAY 339

Paint Paths

Rapunzel needs some paints for her next work of art. Look at the list below, then find a path that contains exactly what she needs.

Paints needed:
2x pink, 1x yellow,
3x green, 1x blue

Jigsaw Jumble

Can you work out where each of these puzzle pieces belong to complete the picture of Moana and the ocean?

DAY 340

DAY
341

The Real Aurora
Which image below is really Aurora?
Follow the clues to find out!

Clues

1. Aurora is not wearing a blue glove

2. Aurora is wearing her crown

3. Aurora's necklace is not silver

DAY
342

Set the Scene

In the space behind Tiana, draw a New Orleans scene!

Once Upon a Time...

Write an exciting story about Jasmine!

Badge Patterns

Complete the patterns below by filling the empty spaces with the correct badges!

a **b**

c **d**

1

2

3

Snow Sequences

Can you help Snow White to find these sequences in the grid?

a

b

c

d

Bubble Count

How many bubbles are there around Ariel and Flounder?

There are .... bubbles!

Nature Colouring

Use your best pens and pencils to decorate this scene of Pocahontas enjoying nature!

Spot the Difference

There are six differences between these images of Belle.
Look closely and see if you can spot them all!

Dragon Puzzle

Can you work out which boxes should contain dragon badges and which shouldn't? The numbers tell you how many badges there should be in each row and column. Start with row 'o' and add the Xs!

Close Friends

Look at the close-ups, then see if you can spot which Pub Thug they belong to.

a   b   c   d   e

1   2   3   4   5

Follow your Destiny

Which path will lead Moana to Te Fiti and help her to restore the mother island?

DAY 351

a
b
c

DAY 352

Who Said That?

Do you remember who said the quotes below? Fill in the empty spaces to show who said them.

1 ....
2 ....
3 ....
4 ....

a Lucify not funny. Lucify mean.

b Just leave it to me, what a gown this will be!

c Oh no, wait, you can't go now, it's only—

d I see no reason why you can't go... if you get all your work done.

DAY
353

Noughts and Crosses

Playing with a friend, choose who will be noughts and who will be crosses. Then, take it in turns to fill empty spaces in the grid. The winner is the first person to get three in a row horizontally, vertically or diagonally.

DAY
354

Beach Walk

Colour Ariel, Max and Seashell to complete this beach scene!

Castle Changes

One of the smaller pictures of Merida's bedroom is slightly different to the bigger image. Which one?

Flower Finder

Help Aurora to count how many of each flower there are in the jumble!

a ....

b ....

c ....

d ....

Picture Puzzle

This picture needs putting back together!
Write the letters in the empty boxes below
to show where each piece belongs.

a
b
c
d
e
f
g
h

c
....
....
....
....
....
....
....

Path for a Prince

Help the Prince through the maze to
Belle, making sure to follow the sequence
shown at the bottom of the page.

START

FINISH

Sequence to follow:

Shadow Match

Which shadow exactly matches the bigger picture of Rapunzel?

a   b   c   d

Mulan Maths

Help Mulan to fill in the empty spaces in the pyramid by adding together the numbers in the two boxes immediately below!

2

3 2   1 3

How Many Words?

How many times can you count the word **MOANA** in the grid? Write your answer below.

Moana appears
....
times!

K	E	R	M	F	P	X	D	Y
G	B	M	O	A	N	A	K	M
M	O	U	D	P	M	I	E	H
O	J	Z	F	I	O	T	O	B
A	M	O	A	N	A	S	M	H
N	N	Q	R	C	N	S	O	V
A	U	T	S	O	A	E	A	W
R	P	A	L	M	O	A	N	A
G	M	O	A	N	A	S	A	W

Quick Quiz

Read the questions and see how well you know *Pocahontas*!

1. From which city did the ship carrying the settlers leave?

....

2. What is the name of the talking tree spirit?

....

3. What do the settlers believe is buried in Pocahontas' home?

....

4. What is the name of Pocahontas' pet raccoon?

....

5. Who did Pocahontas' necklace originally belong to?

....

Scene Sorter

Can you put this scene back in order by labelling the pieces from 1 to 5?

a

....

b

....

c

....

d

....

e

....

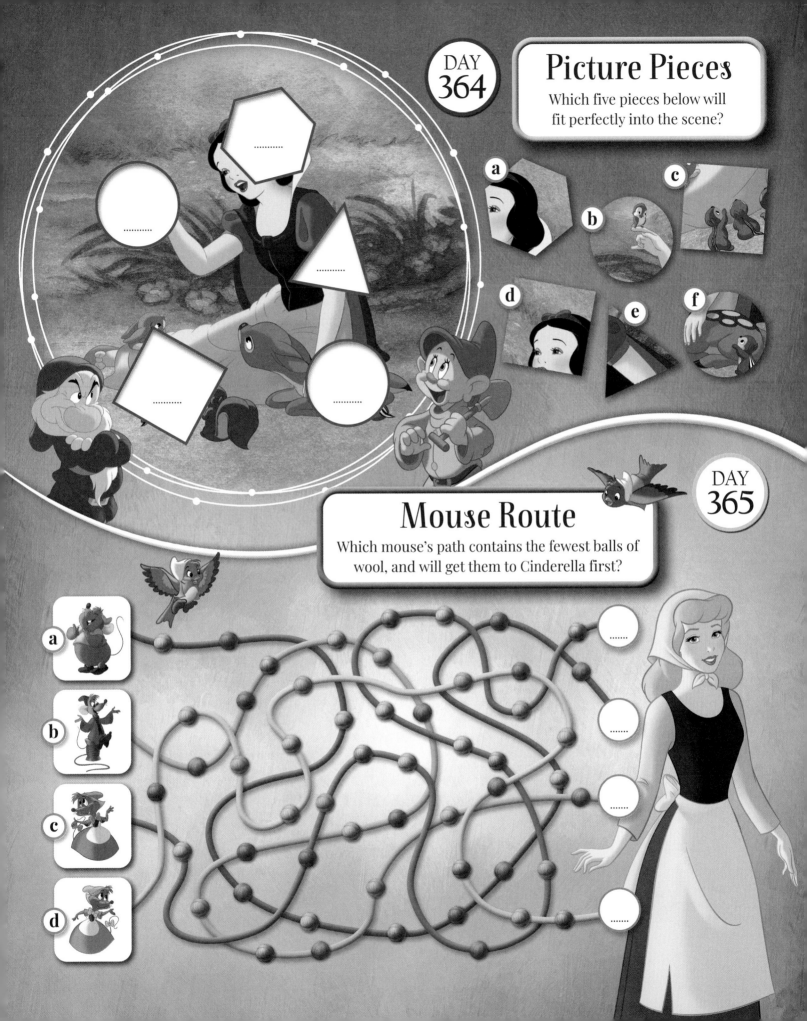

Picture Pieces

Which five pieces below will fit perfectly into the scene?

a

b

c

d

e

f

Mouse Route

Which mouse's path contains the fewest balls of wool, and will get them to Cinderella first?

a

b

c

d

Answers

Day 1 – Puzzling Picture

Day 2 – Mermaid Differences
Picture c is the odd one out

Day 4 – Mouse Maze

Day 5 – Merida Mix-up

2, 12, 4, 15, 9, 6, 8

Day 6 – Servant Shadows
a-3, b-4, c-2, d-1

Day 7 – Pretty Patterns
1-c, 2-d, 3-b, 4-a

Day 9 – Which Lamp?

Day 10 – Snow Scramble
DOPEY, DOC, GRUMPY, SNEEZY, BASHFUL, HAPPY, SLEEPY

Day 11 – Perfect Palette
Palette d matches exactly

Day 13 – Cinderella Close-ups

Day 14 – Spot the Difference

Day 15 – Te Fiti Track

Day 16 – Sea Sudoku

Day 17 – Beautiful Butterflies
27 Purple Butterflies
30 Pink Butterflies

Day 18 – Friend Finder
1-g, 2-b, 3-c, 4-e, 5-d

Day 19 – Tiana Changes
Picture a is different

Day 21 – Trouble Trail
1-e, 2-d, 3-f, 4-b, 5-a

Day 23 – The Real Belle
Picture c is Belle

Day 24 – Take Note

Day 25 – Fan Finder

Day 26 – Princess Puzzle

Day 27 – Jigsaw Jumble
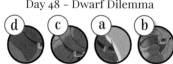

Day 28 – Treasure Tracker
a-5, b-5, c-7, d-8, e-10

Day 29 – Bottle Bubbles
Bubble e contains all the bottles

Day 31 – Prince Paths
Path d will get there the quickest

Day 32 – Adventurer Shadows
Shadow b matches exactly

Day 33 – A Small Change
Picture a is different

Day 34 – Castle Close-ups
Close-up d doesn't belong in the scene

Day 35 – Sequence Search

Day 36 – Domino Dash
a-3, b-2, c-1, d-5, c-4

Day 37 – Dinner Time!
a-3, b-2, c-1

Day 38 – Picture Jumble
a-2, b-5, c-3, d-4, e-1

Day 40 – Which Bone?
Bone c belongs to Little Brother

Day 42 – Silhouette Sorter
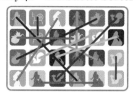

Day 43 – Father Finds
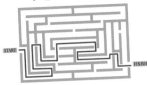

Day 44 – Carpet Copy
Picture c matches exactly

Day 45 – Bingo with Belle
Bingo card d matches exactly

Day 46 – Chameleon Counter

Day 48 – Dwarf Dilemma
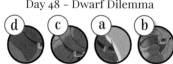

Day 49 – Mermaid Maths
a-4, b-7, c-3, d-11

Day 51 – Memorable Scene
1-Six, 2-Green, 3-No, 4-Aubergine, bread, green chilli, cheese, red pepper or fish, 5-Two

Day 52 – Real Little Brother
Picture c is Little Brother

Day 53 – Spot the Difference

Day 55 – Marketplace Mayhem

Day 56 – Royal Flag Route

Day 57 – Height Help
a-3, b-4, c-1, d-2, e-6, f-5

Day 58 – Will o' the Wisp Way

Day 59 – Post Pile
There are 8 blue envelopes with purple stamps

Day 60 – Snow White Sequences
1-c, 2-a, 3-e, 4-f, 5-d, 6-b

Day 61 – Mulan Message
BE YOUR OWN HERO

Day 62 – Food Favourites
a-3, b-2, c-1

Day 65 – Word Finder
Jasmine appears 5 times

Day 66 – Mermaid Match
Pictures b, e and f match

Day 68 – Companion Counting
There are 14 mice

Day 70 – Shadow of a Hero
Shadow c matches exactly

Answers

Day 72 – Bird Trail

Day 74 – Beautiful Birds
There are 27 birds

Day 75 – Tiana Track

Day 76 – Baking Differences

Day 78 – Pet Poses
a-6, b-9, c-5, d-8

Day 79 – Ariel's Treasures

Day 80 – Set Sail!

Day 81 – Jigsaw Joy

Day 82 – Dancing Difference
Picture a is different

Day 87 – Scene It All
1-Four, 2-Brown, 3-No, 4-Stone

Day 88 – Perfect Puzzle

Day 89 – Triton Trail
Path b has the most icons

Day 90 – Mess Mayhem

Day 91 – Pocahontas Path

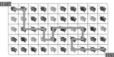

Day 92 – Magic Mirror Match
Shadow a matches exactly

Day 94 – I am Moana!

Day 95 – Canine Chase

Day 96 – Odd Animal Out
The frog appears once

Day 97 – Picture Pieces
a-4, b-5, c-1, d-3, e-2

Day 98 – Magic Maths
a=9, b=2, c=12

Day 99 – Exploring Fun
a-6, b-7, c-5, d-7, e-8

Day 100 – Scottish Secret
OUR FATE LIVES WITHIN US

Day 102 – Wool Way

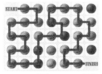

Day 103 – Diamond Dash
Path a will get to Snow White the quickest

Day 105 – Moana Mystery
Picture c is Moana

Day 106 – Footprint Finder
a-2, b-3, c-1

Day 107 – Shadow Showdown
Shadow b matches exactly

Day 108 – Spot the Difference

Day 110 – Quote Quiz
1-d, 2-b, 3-a, 4-c

Day 111 – Mother Maze

Day 112 – Culinary Changes

Day 115 – Sunflower Sizes
a-1, b-4, c-6, d-3, e-5, f-2, g-7

Day 116 – Lost Property
a-1, b-3, c-2

Day 118 – What a Mess!
a-9 spoons, b-10 plates, c-13 bowls

Day 119 – Odd One Out
Close-up b isn't part of the picture

Day 120 – Fairy Sudoku

Day 121 – Royal Route

Day 122 – Monkeying Around!
Shadow c doesn't have a match

Day 123 – Jigsaw Jumble

Day 125 – Pumpkin Bingo
Bingo card e matches Cinderella's

Day 127 – Who Said It?
1-b, 2-c, 3-a, 4-d

Day 128 – Seahorse Search

Day 129 – Royal Close-ups
Close-up b isn't part of the scene

Day 130 – Dwarf Dial
DOPEY

Day 131 – Belle's Books

Day 132 – Coordinate Chaos
a-(4,b), b-(4,d), c-(3,c),
d-(1,d), e-(4,a), f-(1,c)

Day 133 – Palace Paths
Paths e and f equal 20

Day 134 – Spot the Difference

Day 136 – Statue Search
There are 9 statues

Day 138 – Follow the Fans

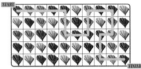

Day 139 – Maurice Maze
Path c will lead to Maurice

Day 141 – Sequence Search

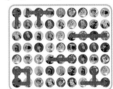

Day 142 – Snow Shadows
Shadow e matches exactly

Day 144 – Stargazers
There are 28 stars

Day 145 – Name Scramble
a-Tiana, b-Charlotte, c-Naveen,
d-Louis, e-Eudora

Day 146 – Merida Mix-up
Picture b is Merida

Day 147 – Light the Way

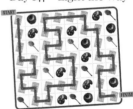

Day 149 – On Their Own

Day 150 – Rowing Route
Path c is the best route

Day 153 – Forest Friends
Close-up c doesn't belong

Answers

Day 154 – Triplet Trivia
1-True, 2-False, 3-False, 4-True, 5-True

Day 157 – Letter Line
TAMATOA

Day 158 – Cushion Chaos

Day 159 – Pup Poses
a-4, b-3, c-6

Day 161 – Cinderella Code
DREAMS DO COME TRUE

Day 162 – Kitchen Clues

Day 163 – Pooch Patterns
1-d, 2-c, 3-a

Day 164 – Missing Belle
Picture e does not have a shadow

Day 165 – Scene Changes
Picture a is different

Day 167 – The Missing Piece
Piece f will complete the scene

Day 168 – Princess Pyramid

		27		
	13		14	
	6	7	7	
3	3	4	3	
2	1	2	2	1

Day 169 – Picture Pieces

Day 170 – Real Rapunzel
Picture c is Rapunzel

Day 172 – Friend Differences

Day 173 – Petal Puzzle
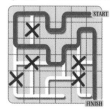

Day 174 – Mermaid Mirror
MAKE YOUR VOICE HEARD

Day 175 – Quick Quiz
1-Maui, 2-Pua, 3-Baby turtle, 4-Motunui, 5-His magical fish hook

Day 176 – It's a Match
Shadow a matches exactly

Day 178 – Powhatan Path
Path b adds up to 20

Day 179 – How Many Words?
Mulan appears 9 times

Day 180 – Cupcake Counter
a-6, b-4, c-12, d-8, e-3, f-9
Total cupcakes: 42

Day 182 – Pattern Pals
1-b, 2-c, 3-a

Day 183 – Hit the Bullseye!
Sum c will help Merida hit the bullseye

Day 184 – Who Said That?
1-d, 2-c, 3-a, 4-b

Day 186 – Chase your Dreams

Day 187 – Compass Clutter
Compass c appears only once

Day 190 – Tangle of Wisps
a-5, b-6, c-4

Day 191 – Diamond Dash

Day 194 – Path of a Princess

Day 195 – Mushu Maze
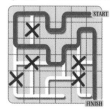

Day 196 – Royal Celebrations

Day 197 – Perfect Pyramid

		26		
	12		14	
	5	7	7	
2	3	4	3	
1	1	2	2	1

Day 200 – Bird Bubble
Bubble c contains all the birds

Day 201 – Silhouette Sorter
a-2, b-3, c-5, d-4, e-1

Day 202 – Moana Message
WE WERE VOYAGERS

Day 203 – Food Favourites
1-b, 2-a, 3-c

Day 205 – Forest Finds
a-14, b-5, c-4, d-7

Day 206 – Which Wool?
Basket a matches exactly

Day 207 – Quick Quiz
1-Ping, 2-Her father's, 3-Cri-Kee, 4- The Imperial City, 5-A horse

Day 210 – Merida Match

Day 211 – On Their Own

Day 212 – Dinner Differences

Day 214 – Who Said It?
1-d, 2-a, 3-c, 4-b

Day 215 – The Missing Piece
Piece a will complete the scene

Day 216 – Ready or Not, Here I Come!

Day 217 – Shopping Search
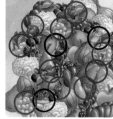

Day 218 – Letter Line
FAUNA

Day 220 – Scene It All
1-Red, 2-No, 3-Yes, 4-No, 5-One

Day 221 – Cottage Coordinates
1-(3,b), 2-Worms, 3-Two, 4-One, 5-(5,c)

Day 223 – Missing Genie
Box c is missing a picture

Day 225 – Lost Letters
LUMIERE, COGSWORTH, MAURICE, THE BEAST, MRS POTTS, GASTON

Day 226 – Maui Maze

Day 227 – Odd One Out
Image a is the odd one out

Day 228 – The Race Home
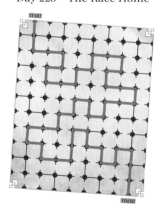

Answers

Day 229 - Picture Pieces
a-2, b-4, c-1, d-5, e-3

Day 230 - Treasure Trove

Day 232 - Slipper Search
Path c is all the same colour

Day 233 - Love Note
I'LL ALWAYS BE WITH YOU

Day 234 - Palace Path

Day 235 - Party Prep
Number of roses: 37
Number of tables: 7

Day 239 - Mirror Message
SOMETIMES OUR STRENGTHS LIE
BENEATH THE SURFACE

Day 240 - Perfect Pal
Picture d matches exactly

Day 241 - Search and Find

Day 242 - Milliner Maths
a=8, b=11, c=4, d=9

Day 244 - Escape Route

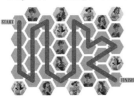

Day 245 - Scene It!
Scene d is different

Day 246 - Nuisance Napkins
The yellow napkin only appears once

Day 248 - Pocahontas Paths
NAKOMA

Day 250 - True Shadow
Shadow c matches

Day 251 - Who Said That?
a-5, b-4, c-2, d-1, e-3

Day 252 - Snow's Search

Day 253 - Pretty Pairs

Day 254 - Wardrobe Way
Cinderella will choose outfit 2

Day 256 - Perfect Picture

Day 257 - Counting Corn
a-2, b-3, c-4, d-5

Day 259 - Song Sequences
a-5, b-3, c-2

Day 260 - How Many Times?
Merida appears 6 times

Day 262 - Snow Scene
1-Yes, 2-Red, 3-Four

Day 263 - Silly Shapes

Day 264 - Odd One Out
Picture b is different

Day 266 - Monkey Mayhem
Picture f is the odd one out

Day 267 - Find Your Way

Day 268 - Memory Muddle
The pin cushion has been
removed from Jumble 2

Day 269 - Badge Blunder

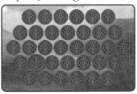

Day 270 - Musical Mermaids
Mermaid d will get the solo

Day 271 - Cupcake Clues

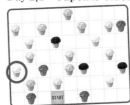

Day 272 - Name Scramble
1-Shang, 2-Mulan, 3-Mushu, 4-Khan

Day 273 - Odd One Out
Picture a is the odd one out

Day 274 - True or False?
1-False, 2-True, 3-True, 4-False, 5-False

Day 276 - Pocahontas Poses
Box c is missing a picture

Day 279 - A Real Princess
Picture e is Snow White

Day 280 - Character Counter
Merryweather appears the most

Day 281 - Sword Sums
a=2, b=3, c=1, 4=10

Day 282 - Flynn's Favourite Food
Path d will lead Flynn to Rapunzel

Day 283 - Close-up Chaos
a-3, b-4, c-1, d-2

Day 286 - Domino Dash
a-2, b-3, c-1

Day 287 - Save Snow White
Formation b fits perfectly

Day 288 - Movie Moments
a-4, b-3, c-1, d-2

Day 289 - Star Search

Day 290 - Quick Quiz
1-Major, 2-Boo, 3-The Grand Duke,
4-Drizella and Anastasia, 5-A mouse

Day 291 - Close-up Royalty
a-4, b-2, d-1, e-3, f-5
Close-up c doesn't belong in the scene

Day 293 - Castle Code
TALE AS OLD AS TIME

Day 295 - Frame Finder

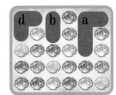

Day 296 - Shell Stacker
Pieces a, b and d fit perfectly

Day 297 - Attack of the Pirates
appears 6 times

Day 298 - Odd One Out
Shadow c is the odd one out

Day 299 - Perfect Setting
1-c, 2-a, 3-b, 4-e, 5-d

Day 300 - Magical Mazes

Answers

Day 301 – Who Said That?
1-c, 2-b, 3-e, 4-a, 5-d

Day 303 – True Shoes
Slippers f and j match

Day 304 – Spot the Difference

Day 305 – Picture Jumble
a-3 , b-5 , c- 1, d-4 , e-2

Day 306 – Reading Route

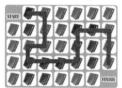

Day 307 – Time for Tea
Bubble a contains all the teapots

Day 308 – Firework Finds

Day 310 – Treasure Hunt

Day 311 – Perfect Puzzle

Day 312 – Letter Lines
VLADIMIR

Day 313 – Pocahontas Patterns
1-d, 2-b, 3-a

Day 314 – Charlotte Clues
Picture b is Charlotte

Day 316 – Royal Route
1-d, 2-a, 3-b, 4-c

Day 317 – True or False?
1-True, 2-False, 3-False, 4-True,
5-False

Day 318 – Memorable Scene
1-Yes, 2-Three, 3-Purple, 4-No

Day 319 – Number Paths
Paths c and g equal 20

Day 320 – Perfect Pearl

Day 323 – Pocahontas Pictures
Picture c is different

Day 324 – Sequence Search

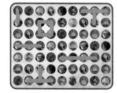

Day 325 – Mother Maze

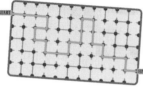

Day 326 – Quick Quiz
1-Doc and Dopey, 2-The Huntsman,
3-Diamonds, 4-Soup, 5-The Prince

Day 327 – A Perfect Match
Picture c matches the bigger picture

Day 328 – Castle Coordinates
1-(4,a), 2-(2,a), 3-(1,b), 4-Flag, 5-(3,a)

Day 329 – Butterfly Bingo
Bingo card e matches Aurora's

Day 330 – How Many Times?
Ariel appears 6 times

Day 331 – Belle Maze

Day 332 – Princess Pottery

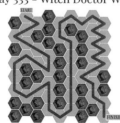

Day 333 – Witch Doctor Way

Day 335 – Memory Muddle
The bowl has been removed
from Jumble 2

Day 336 – Snow Secret
BE A FRIEND YOU CAN TRUST

Day 338 – Nature Numbers
a=1, b=13, c=2, d=6

Day 339 – Paint Paths
Path b contains all the paints needed

Day 340 –Jigsaw Jumble

Day 341 – The Real Aurora
Picture c is Aurora

Day 344 – Badge Patterns
1-d, 2-a, 3-c

Day 345 – Snow Sequences

Day 346 – Bubble Count
There are 23 bubbles

Day 348 – Spot the Difference

Day 349 – Dragon Puzzle

Day 350 – Close Friends
a-4, b-3, c-1, d-5, e-2

Day 351 – Follow your Destiny
Path c leads to Te Fiti

Day 352 – Who Said That?
a-4, b-2, c-3, d-1

Day 355 – Castle Changes
Picture a is different

Day 356 – Flower Finder
a-6, b-4, c-4, d-5

Day 357 – Picture Puzzle

Day 358 – Path for a Prince

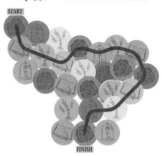

Day 359 – Shadow Match
Shadow c matches exactly

Day 360 – Mulan Maths

Day 361 – How Many Words?
Moana appears 7 times

Day 362 – Quick Quiz
1-London, 2-Grandmother Willow,
3-Gold, 4-Meeko, 5-Her mother

Day 363 – Scene Sorter
a-4, b-1, c-5, d-2, e-3

Day 364 – Picture Pieces

Day 365 – Mouse Route
Path a will get to Cinderella first